The first carts were made by the Sumerians, after they invented the wheel around 4000 B.C. The carts had solid wheels turning on a fixed axle and were drawn by a type of wild donkey.

Eventually, the solid wheel was replaced with a spoked wheel. By 2000 B.C., horses were being used to pull loads in China.

When the Vikings began raiding Europe, they found horses and carts invaluable for transporting people and weapons over the rough tracks of the Alps.

This illustration shows the first bus. Towards the end of the Medieval age, carts equipped with a hodometer were used. The hodometer measured the number of turns of a wheel and thus the "fare" was calculated.

Another use of the horse and cart was in the mines of Britain and Germany. Things were made easier for the horses with the laying of rails, first wooden, then metal.

By 1800, stage coaches were being used to transport people and goods. The coaches were sprung and were drawn by two pairs of horses.

JUDY '78

ROD STEWART

# Simple Simon

**H**ERE'S how to make a useful draught excluder for your bedroom—and all the materials you need can be found around the house.

You will need:— clean, laddered tights and/or stockings, scraps of lightweight material, a large remnant of material and pieces of ribbon and felt.

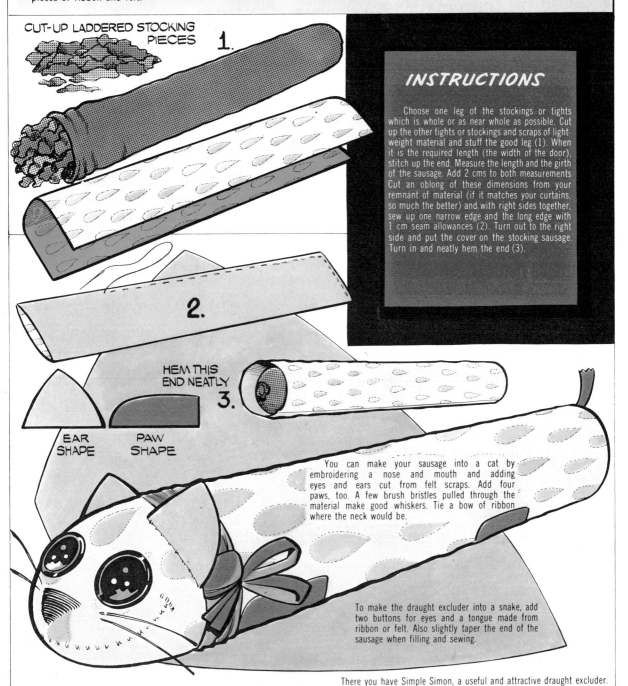

CUT-UP LADDERED STOCKING PIECES

**1.**

**2.**

**3.**

HEM THIS END NEATLY

EAR SHAPE

PAW SHAPE

## INSTRUCTIONS

Choose one leg of the stockings or tights which is whole or as near whole as possible. Cut up the other tights or stockings and scraps of lightweight material and stuff the good leg (1). When it is the required length (the width of the door), stitch up the end. Measure the length and the girth of the sausage. Add 2 cms to both measurements Cut an oblong of these dimensions from your remnant of material (if it matches your curtains, so much the better) and, with right sides together, sew up one narrow edge and the long edge with 1 cm seam allowances (2). Turn out to the right side and put the cover on the stocking sausage. Turn in and neatly hem the end (3).

You can make your sausage into a cat by embroidering a nose and mouth and adding eyes and ears cut from felt scraps. Add four paws, too. A few brush bristles pulled through the material make good whiskers. Tie a bow of ribbon where the neck would be.

To make the draught excluder into a snake, add two buttons for eyes and a tongue made from ribbon or felt. Also slightly taper the end of the sausage when filling and sewing.

There you have Simple Simon, a useful and attractive draught excluder.

# Santa's Sleigh

THIS Christmas sleigh makes a pretty decoration for any Christmas table and it's easy to make.

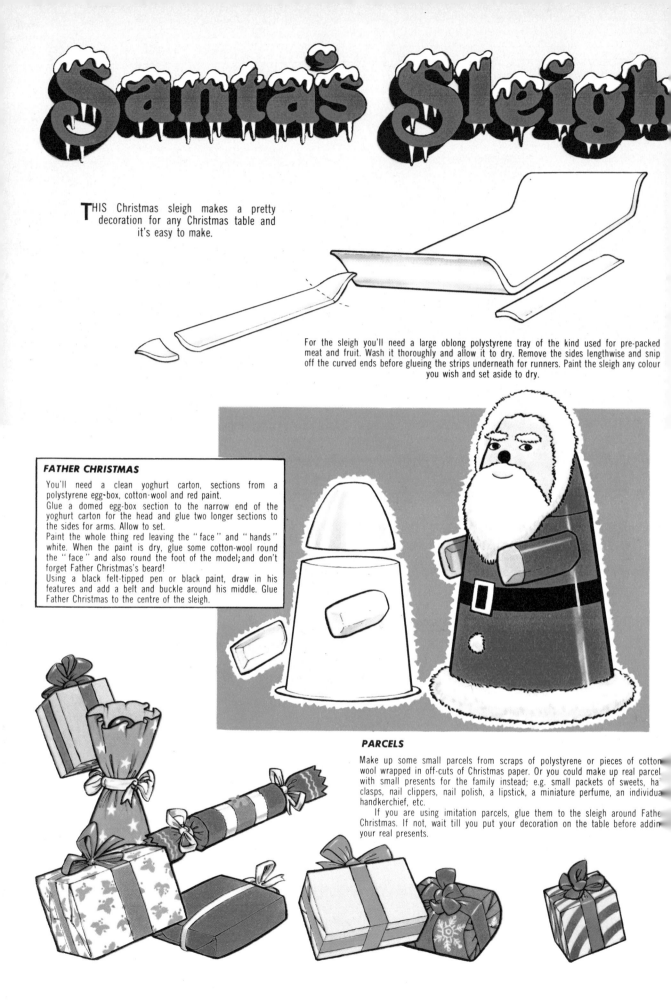

For the sleigh you'll need a large oblong polystyrene tray of the kind used for pre-packed meat and fruit. Wash it thoroughly and allow it to dry. Remove the sides lengthwise and snip off the curved ends before glueing the strips underneath for runners. Paint the sleigh any colour you wish and set aside to dry.

## FATHER CHRISTMAS

You'll need a clean yoghurt carton, sections from a polystyrene egg-box, cotton-wool and red paint.

Glue a domed egg-box section to the narrow end of the yoghurt carton for the head and glue two longer sections to the sides for arms. Allow to set.

Paint the whole thing red leaving the "face" and "hands" white. When the paint is dry, glue some cotton-wool round the "face" and also round the foot of the model; and don't forget Father Christmas's beard!

Using a black felt-tipped pen or black paint, draw in his features and add a belt and buckle around his middle. Glue Father Christmas to the centre of the sleigh.

## PARCELS

Make up some small parcels from scraps of polystyrene or pieces of cotton wool wrapped in off-cuts of Christmas paper. Or you could make up real parcel with small presents for the family instead; e.g. small packets of sweets, ha clasps, nail clippers, nail polish, a lipstick, a miniature perfume, an individua handkerchief, etc.

If you are using imitation parcels, glue them to the sleigh around Fathe Christmas. If not, wait till you put your decoration on the table before addin your real presents.

## RUDOLPH THE REINDEER

To make Rudolph the Reindeer you'll need a cardboard toilet-roll centre, 1 or 2 polystyrene egg-boxes, a length of soft toilet-roll or kitchen roll or a scrap of brown material big enough to cover the toilet-roll centre loosely, and some wool or ribbon.

**EARS**

**ANTLERS**

**1**

**2**

**3**

Take one section of an egg-box and squash it in half once (1), then again (2). Glue a piece of the egg-box between the second fold to form the neck (3). Cut some antlers from the egg-box making them as branched as possible. Cut two ear shapes from the polystyrene, too. Make four small slits in the head and insert the two sets of antlers and ears with a little dab of glue. Cut two forelegs and two rear legs from the flat lids of the egg-boxes. Make four slits in the bottom of the toilet-roll centre and one on top where the head will sit. Insert the four legs and the head section into the slits with a little glue.

When glue is dry, paint the antlers, ears, head and legs. Don't forget his red nose!

**FORELEGS SHAPES**

**REAR LEGS SHAPES**

Paint the kitchen roll or toilet-roll brown and allow it to dry. Wrap the " coat " around the cardboard roll, tucking it in slightly at the front and rear. Either glue or stitch together underneath. Make a small tail from wool or cotton-wool and stitch it in place.

Make reins from ribbon or crocheted chains as shown in the illustration. If you have a small bell, stitch it to the reins at Rudolph's neck and there's Santa's Sleigh all ready for the table.

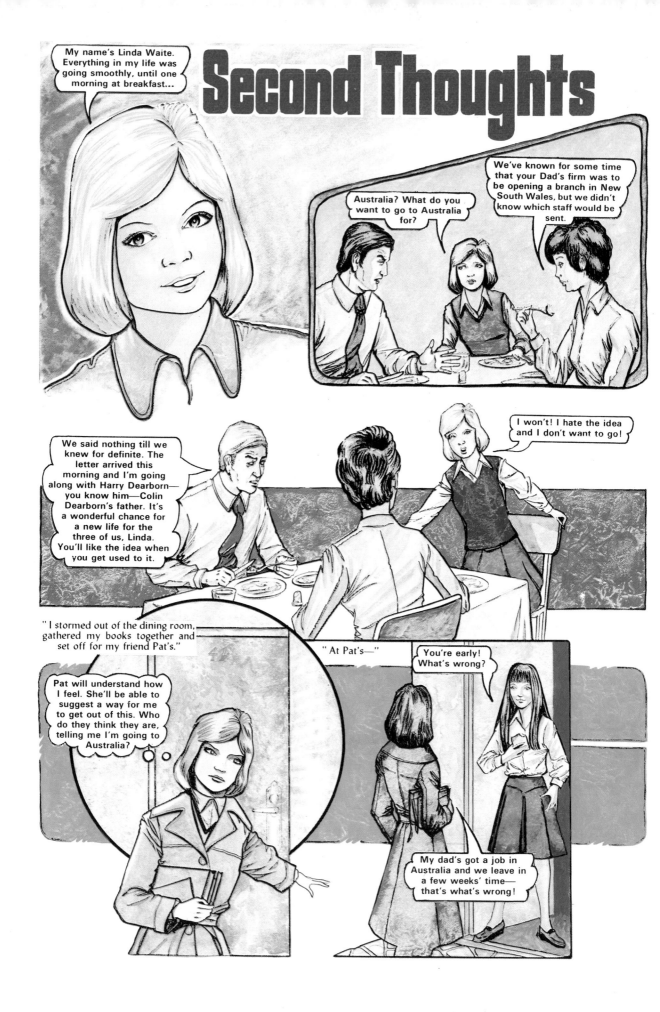

# WEE SLAVEY

NELLIE PERKS was a young maid in the Victorian household of Sir William Selby Smythe and his family. One evening, there was great excitement in the house.

The young guests are arriving for Master Algy's birthday party, Cook.

Yes, Nellie. But we have work to do below stairs.

I'll take this lot upstairs, Nellie.

All right, Cook. I'll get the next tray ready.

Just then—

This bag is for Signor Bellossi, miss.

But there's no Signor Bellossi in this house.

I can't help that! I'm only a messenger, and I was told to bring the bag here.

SIGNOR BELLOSSI

Lawks, it's a ventriloquist's dummy! Now I know it's been brought to the wrong address!

# Shorty

I KNOW I'm short. Five foot nothing, in fact, but there was no need for everybody to go on about it.

"You're petite, like me," said my Aunt Beryl—and who wants to be like Aunt Beryl?

"Petite?" scoffed my brother, Tim. "Let's be truthful; Sheila's stunted, to match her brain."

"Never mind, love," said my mum. "Little and good, is what I say."

It wouldn't have been so bad, only in the last year all my friends had shot up like bean-poles. My best friend, Anne, is slim and tall and willowy, and when I stumped along beside her, just reaching to her shoulder, I felt I could die with envy.

You ought to have seen me in my bedroom—no, on second thoughts, perhaps not, because I must have looked a fool—stretching up on tiptoe; doing mad exercises; jumping off a stool to hang by my fingertips from the top of my cupboard; anything to get those extra inches. Not that it ever worked.

Anne had just started showing interest in boys, and if we were walking home together I heard of nothing else but her latest conquest. Not that we were often alone; there were usually at least two boys with us, laughing and kidding and showing off.

With us, did I say? With Anne, I meant. I have nice reddish-brown hair and blue eyes, but I might just as well not have existed. Just dumpy little Sheila, and all the fun and jokes went on

over my head—literally! I told myself I wasn't interested in boys anyway, but I wasn't very convincing.

Take Simon Bartlett, for instance. Nearly six feet tall, and marvellously good-looking. Anne had been to the disco with him three times, and didn't seem to realise how lucky she was. She was keener on Brian Foster at the time.

"I'd ask Simon to take you out, Sheila," she said, "only he told me he doesn't like going out with short girls." So that put me in my place.

Now I bet I know what you're thinking. "Why on earth does she keep on about being short? Why not buy a pair of shoes with really high platform soles?" Why not, indeed? Dad, that's why.

"Stupid fashion," he said. "I'm not having you clumping round the house like a horse. Dangerous, too."

What's more, Mum always went with me to buy shoes, and wouldn't let me have anything the least bit way-out. But when Anne said that bit about Simon not liking short girls, I made up my mind I'd have a pair of platforms—come what may. Anne had them, of course. Two pairs, in fact. Her parents let her have anything that was in fashion, and I often used to try her things on. You should see me in one of her long skirts!

One day, she showed me a pair of new shoes. They had absolutely outrageous heels—a good four inches high.

"I was an idiot to buy them," she said. "Money wasted. I thought they looked marvellous in the shop, but I didn't realise how tall they made me. I wore them last night and I was taller than Brian by a good inch. That doesn't do anything for a bloke's ego, believe me."

I was looking wistfully at them, and she suddenly pushed them towards me.

"Go on, Sheila," she said. "Try them. You're always moaning about being too short."

I kicked off my own shoes and climbed on to the platform ones, because that was what it felt like —climbing. I stood there, wobbling a bit, and looked at the two of us in the mirror.

"I'm nearly as tall as you now," I said, and took a few careful steps around the bedroom.

"Tell you what," said Anne. "You can have them, if you like. I'll never wear them again."

"Can I really?" It was a wonderful feeling up there, and I couldn't wait to try them out on the local boys. Perhaps they'd notice me at last if I were nearer eye level. Especially Simon. But then the excitement left me.

"Mum and Dad would never let me," I said.

Anne looked at me as if I was daft.

"How do they come into it? You don't have to tell them everything, do you? You can keep them round here, and change into them whenever you want to."

The temptation was too great.

"Thanks, Anne," I said, and we finished up the evening with a try-out round the park. I felt quite peculiar, like being on stilts. I had to walk stiff-legged, and everything looked different, as though I was peering down from a high mountain. I could feel the muscles in the backs of my calves beginning to ache like mad, but I wasn't going to let on.

"This is marvellous!" I said.

## A DIFFERENT PERSON

I COULDN'T wear them to school, of course. The Head had a very strict ruling, after Melanie Jones broke her ankle on the stairs, so during school hours I was still mousy little Sheila Abbott, knee-high to a grasshopper.

But in the evenings I was a different person. Once I was up on those heels I was laughing and kidding with the best of them.

When we had any money left we used to go round to the Go-Go Coffee Bar—there was always a good crowd there. One evening, when we were sitting at a table with a mixed bag of kids from school, I suddenly nudged Anne.

"Look!" I whispered. "See who's just come in?"

It was Simon, and he strolled across to the counter with that lordly air as though the place belonged to him. Now was my chance.

"I'm going to get some more sugar," I gabbled hastily, and getting up, I teetered across to where he was leaning on the counter.

"Hello, Simon," I said as I got to him, and he turned and gave me a smile that turned my knees to water. And then I realised that his smile was going straight past me, across my left shoulder.

"Hi, there!" he said, as a most gorgeous girl, all gleaming teeth and green eye-shadow, came up behind me. She gave me a look that would have withered a pot plant, and pushed in between me and Simon.

He hadn't even seen me. Wishing there were some quick way out of the coffee bar, preferably through a crack in the floorboards, I grabbed a couple of lumps of sugar and went back to our table.

"I tried to stop you," said Anne. "That's Margo Bentley. Simon's been going steady with her for weeks."

All the kids at the table were grinning.

"I'm going home. Got some history to do," I mumbled, and strutted out of the Go-Go with my head in the air. I was still a bit clumsy on those high heels and I bumped into a chair on the way out.

"Sorry," I said automatically,

and the quiet boy, sitting there on his own, gave me a shy smile. He wasn't one of our gang, but I felt sure I'd seen him somewhere before.

I kept away from the coffee bar after that.

"Don't be silly," said Anne. "Can't you take a joke?"

Even she didn't realise how I still squirmed and went hot all over every time I thought what a fool I'd looked. I just didn't want to be with anyone who had witnessed it, and I dreaded running into that Margo person again. As most of my friends, including Anne, still drifted round to the Go-Go fairly often, I found myself on my own a good deal.

The platform shoes stayed in my bag in a corner of my cupboard, and I went back to being mousy Sheila Abbott again. Being ignored. And I didn't like it a bit. I had enjoyed being that different me; four inches taller, with cramp in my calves and a tendency to turn my ankles if I hurried.

One evening, when I was going round to the library, I thought I'd try them again. I took my shoulder bag, and as soon as I was away from our street, I slipped into a shop doorway and changed into the high heels.

I could feel the difference immediately; I walked along with my head up and got wolf whistles from a couple of boys on the corner.

When I got into the library I noticed a boy sitting at one of the tables, writing away in a notebook with a most studious air. Of course! The quiet boy in the coffee bar; I knew I'd seen him before—he was often in the library, doing his homework by the look of it.

Just my luck—beginning to get my self-confidence back, and I had to run into someone who had been at the Scene of my Humiliation. Yes, I can laugh about it now, but then I was still so sore that I could only remember it in capital letters.

I changed my books, grabbing the first two that came to hand, but while I was waiting to have them stamped I saw the boy look up, and although I kept my head turned away I could feel that he was trying to catch my eye.

As soon as I could, I snatched up my books and dashed for the door, wrenched it open and started down the stone steps to the pavement. High heels, I discovered, are all right for careful walking but a dead loss in a hurry.

I tripped halfway down, grabbed for the handrail, missed it, and went sprawling down the remaining three steps to the pavement, scattering my belongings all round me. I heard the door open again and running feet coming down the steps.

"Are you hurt?" asked a voice, and there was the quiet boy, bending over me.

"I think I've broken every bone in my body," I said, struggling to sit up; but seeing the concern on his face I managed a feeble laugh. "Not really," I said. "Banged both knees and

ruined a good pair of tights, but otherwise I think I'm in one piece." He was picking up my books and shoulder bag, and then he knelt beside me again.

"Let me help you up," he said, offering me an arm. He pulled me up until we were both standing, and I saw him properly for the first time—a short, stocky boy with dark hair and brown eyes, looking up at me anxiously.

Yes, up at me. Me, Sheila Abbott—taller than the very first nice-looking boy who had ever taken any notice of me. But then I saw his expression, and I could guess what he was feeling. In a flash I did the most sensible thing I've done for ages.

"These silly shoes made me trip," I said. "Half a tick while I change them—I've got some others in my bag."

I sat down on a low wall, took off the platform shoes, and slipped on my others.

"Ooooh! What a relief!" I said, as I got to my feet again, and now found myself looking up into those brown eyes.

"Your name's Sheila, isn't it? I saw you in the Go-Go the other night and I wanted to speak—I've watched you in the library, too. I'm Graham, by the way, but most people call me Shorty."

There was a wry smile on his face.

"Why?" I asked. "You look about the right height to me."

We had a lot to talk about as he walked home with me. He'd been doing exercises for years to try to grow taller, and we had a good laugh, comparing notes. Well, I shan't need to bother with that cupboard-hanging lark any more, unless Graham starts shooting up suddenly.

I only remembered later, when I was bathing my two sore knees, that I'd left Anne's shoes on the pavement outside the library.

"Suppose I'd better look for them when I meet Graham again tomorrow," I thought. "I can always give them to a jumble sale."

# NOW YOU SEE IT...
## DON'T!

BUT GET A PIECE OF RED CELLOPHANE, A PIECE OF CARD, MAKE AS DESCRIBED AND YOU...

YOU THINK THIS HEADING DOESN'T MAKE SENSE? MAKE YOURSELF A **MAGIC WINDOW** AND ALL WILL BE REVEALED! CUT A PIECE OF STOUT CARD 13 × 10 CMS., MARK A 2 CM. BORDER AND CUT OUT THE CENTRE PORTION. GLUE A PIECE OF RED CELLOPHANE (YOU CAN GET IT AT A STATIONER'S) ACROSS THE HOLE AND YOU'LL FIND THAT THINGS AREN'T WHAT THEY SEEM TO BE. LOOK AT THE TITLE, FOR A START.

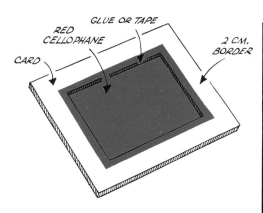

GLUE OR TAPE

RED CELLOPHANE

CARD

2 CM. BORDER

SHE LOOKS HAPPY ENOUGH, BUT VIEW HER THROUGH YOUR 'MAGIC WINDOW' AND SEE WHAT HAPPENS WHEN MUM ASKS IF SHE'S DONE HER HOMEWORK!

A CLOWN COVERS UP HIS FEATURES, BUT **YOU** CAN PIERCE HIS MAKE-UP!

SO YOUR BOYFRIEND HAS BEEN EATING TOO MANY CHOCS? MOVE YOUR 'MAGIC WINDOW' QUICKLY TO AND FRO TO HELP HIM EXERCISE AND GET HIS WEIGHT DOWN!

HIS DAD'S BUILT ON THE SAME LINES, BUT YOUR 'MAGIC WINDOW' WILL SHOW HIS OWN PARTICULAR PROBLEM

I'M AT MY WIT'S END, THE MYSTERY BEING THAT WHEN I EXERCISE ON THIS STOOL TO MAKE SURE THAT MY FAT GOES...

TIDYING UP YOUR BEDROOM AFTER YOU'VE HAD YOUR FRIENDS IN, IS ALWAYS A NUISANCE;

BUT WITH THE HELP OF YOUR 'MAGIC WINDOW'

PRESTO!

## A MAGIC MESSAGE!

MY DOG, JUDY, LIKES BISCUITS, ESPECIALLY IF THEY'RE SOAKED IN MILK. BEST OF ALL, THOUGH, AND HER BIGGEST AND BRIGHTEST TREATS, ARE TO CHASE LITTLE GIRLS AND CHEW UP DAD'S NEWSPAPER!

NOW THAT YOU HAVE THE IDEA, YOU CAN MAKE YOUR OWN MAGIC PICTURES, USING A BLACK AND A RED BALLPOINT OR FELT PENS.

IF YOU'RE NOT TOO GOOD AT DRAWING, TRY WRITING LIKE THIS

PUT YOUR 'MAGIC WINDOW' OVER AND READ THE HIDDEN MESSAGE. OODLES OF FASCINATING FUN AND FREEDOM FROM THAT FED-UP FEELING!

# BOYFRIENDS

"WHAT MAKES THE PERFECT BOYFRIEND? USE THESE CHECK CARDS TO FIND OUT!"

IS HE GOOD-LOOKING? (SCORE 2)

OR JUST A RUGGED CAVEMAN TYPE? (SCORE 3)

**TALL** — SCORE 3 IF YOU'RE TALL. 2 IF MEDIUM 1 IF SHORT

**SHORT** — SCORE 1 IF YOU'RE TALL OR MEDIUM 3 IF SHORT

**MEDIUM** — SCORE 1 IF YOU'RE TALL 3 IF YOU'RE NOT

DOES HE LIKE WHAT **YOU** LIKE — SUCH AS HUMBUGS, GOBSTOPPERS, TOFFEE APPLES, ALL-DAY SUCKERS AND WALNUT WHIPPLES WITH A CHERRY ON TOP?

SCORE 1 FOR EACH ITEM

IS HE PREPARED TO SHARE THEM, RIGHT DOWN TO THE LAST LICK?

IF 'YES', SCORE 5 IF 'NO', DEDUCT 5

## THE MOST IMPORTANT QUESTION OF ALL . . .

DO YOU HAVE TO CHASE **HIM?** (NO SCORE)

OR — YIPPEE — DOES HE CHASE **YOU?** (SCORE 50!)

TO SEE HOW FAST YOU CAN RUN, SHINE A BRIGHT LIGHT ON THE BOTTOM DRAWINGS, LAY AN ORDINARY POCKET COMB ON THEM AND MOVE IT **SLOWLY** ALONG, LIKE THIS —

# YOUR SCORE...

1 TO 10 = LOOK FOR A NEW BOYFRIEND.
10 TO 50 = FAIR, BUT ROOM FOR IMPROVEMENT.
OVER 50 = WOW! YOU HAVE THE PERFECT BOYFRIEND! GRAB A KISS AS YOUR PRIZE!

# Getting the Hump!

**D**URING the Midchester Youth Club's dress rehearsal of their pantomime, Janet Clark sat in the wings thinking how unfair it was that Laura Harris always seemed to be in Andy Rossiter's company, both onstage and off. Suddenly, a voice rang out. It was Janet's brother, Bob, the producer of the show.

Janet! Where are the camel bells?

Oh, sorry, Bob!

About time, too! I've given the cue twice!

Where's your head, Tom? This is supposed to be a dress rehearsal.

It's too stuffy to wear until it's absolutely necessary. I can't breathe in it.

And what are you going to do on the night— suffocate?

Poor Tom! He isn't very good and that costume doesn't help! But I couldn't do it, anyway.

Having remembered Janet's efforts in the previous year's pantomime, Bob had decided to make her stage manager this year–which Janet had thought was marvellous, until she discovered that made her a general dogsbody. But even that wasn't too bad because she could watch Andy Rossiter without anyone noticing, but it made her forget to ring the camel bells and things like that. Not that there had been a camel in the original script! The Youth Club had been gifted a camel costume which Bob thought they had better use, so he wrote the camel into the script.

As Bob and Janet walked home after the rehearsal—

I wish I'd never agreed to do this pantomime. With that stupid, simpering Laura Harris taking up all the stage and that Tom Cleaves—doesn't he know a talking camel's supposed to be funny? He only has one line to say, anyway, and he makes such a mess of it!

Don't worry, Bob. Tom wasn't feeling well tonight. Things'll go fine tomorrow. They say it's best to have a terrible dress rehearsal. It means tomorrow's performance will go off a treat!

Next day, when Bob and Janet arrived at the hall for the show—

Bad news, Bob! Tom Cleaves has 'flu, so no camel, I'm afraid.

What do we do now, Andy? We can't alter the show, but—

Later, when it was Janet's cue—

Good luck, Janet.

Ow!

Sit!

Where? On that chair I suppose.

And what's that thing you've brought with you, Abanazer?

I'm Hamill the camel and you give me the hump!

Stop messing about, Janet! You'll ruin my lines!

Oh, dear! I'm making a right mess of this!

When the scene ended, Janet thought Bob would blow his top, but—

Well done, Janet! Just listen to that applause! You're a success!

I don't think Aladdin agrees with you!

When Janet appeared in a later scene and introduced herself again—

I'm Hamill the camel and you give me the hump!

Give us a song, Hamill!

# TRADER TESS

IN 1890, Tess Taylor was trying to save her Uncle Barney's Brine Shipping Company from ruin. In the West Indies, the Seabird was loading bananas at Port Tobacco.

We should be in for a nice peaceful trip this time, Captain Jones.

Aye, but 'tis bad luck to say it, Miss Tess!

Moments later, Captain Jones turned to walk along the deck.

WAAAAGH!

Cap'n overboard!

He's slipped on a banana skin!

Bad omen. Wet skipper means wet sails. There must be a storm brewing up.

Honestly! You and your omens, Mr Ketch!

But trouble was indeed brewing ashore.

Don't forget the snakes!

One in every bunch, Mister Rumpunch, suh!

Mr Rumpunch was a local agent for Silas Sharp, a rival shipowner.

Hee, hee! Deadly cargo for the Brine Line! A big bonus for me from the Sharp Line!

HISS!

So the Seabird sailed with her hidden stowaways.

Haw, haw! Watch out for dem snakes, boss!

No such things as sea snakes, are there, Skipper?

Course not! Cast off fore and aft!

But, a few days out at sea—

What's wrong with Mrs Grubb?

All ship's cooks are potty!

YAAH! Snakes in my soup!

Banana vipers! Deadliest snakes in the Caribbean!

Gosh, they must have come from the cargo hold!

I'll go down and check the cargo.

Do be careful, Bo'sun Bagwash.

# They've Got The World on a String

A world on strings—that's the DaSilva Puppet Company. Dozens of fascinating fairy-tale characters come to life in their clever hands—Hansel and Gretel, Peter and the Wolf, Pinnochio, Little Joe and many more. Let's take a peep behind the scenes at this world-famous company.

Ray DaSilva's hobby as a boy was making model theatres. Later, with his wife Joan, he put on an English Punch and Judy show at an American Puppet Festival. Then they began to make their own puppets, and, in 1962, came home to England to set up a travelling puppet company.

The puppets are made at the company's headquarters in Godmanchester. Here, Peter Oldham is seen carving a puppet's head, while Joan DaSilva finishes the dress worn by the Wicked Queen in "Snowhite and the Seven Musical Dwarfs".

The voices for the characters in the plays are supplied by professional actors working in a London studio. The musical score is specially composed and arranged to fit in with the story. The completed sound tracks are carefully stored until they are needed for performances all over the country.

Some of the "props" used are very elaborate. This giant fish from "Pinnochio", which swallows first Geppeto, Pinnochio's father, and then Pinnochio himself, has been made specially flexible to give a realistic effect.

The stage used by the DaSilva Company is the largest puppet stage in Britain. Twenty feet high and constructed from aluminium tubing, it allows the use of marionettes from above and glove and rod puppets from below.

Wispa the Wizard appeared in "Jack and the Beanstalk", and, on stage, comes to life so convincingly, it's easy to forget he's a puppet. In fact, some members of the company say they really do wonder sometimes what happens at midnight when there's no one there to see!

The Seven Musical Dwarfs—Doh, Ray, Me, Fah, So, Lah, and Tee—certainly look as if they could dream up all kinds of mischief!

For the DaSilva Puppet Company, the world of puppets is full of fun and excitement. If you are interested in puppets, why not write to the Guild at 17, Tudor Street, London E.C.4 for details? And watch out for the DaSilva Puppet Company when they come your way, bringing with them their magical world on strings!

Photographs by kind permission of the "DaSilva Puppet Company."

# Jane to the Rescue

I've made it. Throw me my jacket, please.

When Jane reached Maureen—

It's all right, Maureen. Lie still. I'm going to the farm to get help.

Sorry, Jane.

When Jane reached the farm—

Jane, whatever's happened? Where's Karen?

Safe. Shepherd's hut . . .

Jane explained what had happened and Aunt Millie soon had the situation under control. Back at the hut—

Everything's going to be all right, Maureen. This is Karen's Aunt Millie— she'll look after you till the ambulance comes. I'll let the others out.

Later that evening, at the hospital—

I'm glad you've come. That was a stupid trick to play on you. I knew you'd be going that way today. I was going to leave a note at the farm saying where you were. How did you manage to get out?

Your sister was right about me being skinny—I managed to squeeze through the window.

I thought I was getting my own back on you, but my sister told me she had lied about what you said and did. She's sorry for being rude. And I'm sorry for being stupid!

Oh, forget it. Let's be friends from now on.

This afternoon's really brought me out of myself. And it made my day when Bob said what a good job it was I'm so slim. Slim sounds so much better than skinny, doesn't it?

# THE OSPREY

## THE FEATHERED FISHERMAN

The osprey is one of Scotland's rarest birds and every year, hundreds of people visit Loch Garten on Speyside, Inverness-shire, where the Royal Society for the Protection of Birds have made the 667 acres of bog and woodland around a nesting tree a bird sanctuary.

Teams of wardens, all volunteers, take it in turns to guard the sanctuary. There, caravans provide their living quarters. Here you see the " hide " where the wardens on the sanctuary take turns in watching the. ospreys.

In this large low hut, the public are able to look at the eyrie through binoculars. On the right is the view from the observation hut.

Both the male and the female make the nest out of sticks, turf and heather. Ospreys pick up any size of wood from 6 inches to 2 feet long.

This is a particularly busy time for the male now, taking food back to the eyrie. The female tends her young for six weeks until they are strong enough to feed themselves.

Eggs, one to three in number are usually laid at the end of April. They are white, beautifully marked with reddish brown and ash grey. Thirty days later, the chicks hatch out.

The ospreys' main food is trout and perch. When hunting, the osprey hovers gracefully over the water, then darts down at a terrific speed, sometimes even plunging into the water before seizing its prey with its powerful talons.

The ospreys spend the winter on the coasts of Southern Europe and Africa, but they are usually back in nesting territory by mid-April.

It is well worth paying a visit to the sanctuary at Loch Garten, especially if you happen to be interested in birds and their habits. There is no admission charge, but there are souvenirs and R.S.P.B. publications on sale.

In 1970, too, Cilla toured Europe, and at Christmas was hostess on BBC TV's "Christmas Night With The Stars" with a guest list headed by Frank Sinatra and Jerry Lewis.

She also won the Sun's award for the Top Female personality in 1970—and she's won it several times since then.

In 1975 she and Bobby, with their two boys, made their fourth round-the-world trip, opening in Australia at Sydney's famous Opera House, then to Los Angeles for Cilla to make her first American recordings. Then, back to Britain for Cilla's Comedy Six—a new venture into comedy sketches.

This is a new me, folks—a non-singing, non-dancing Cilla, acting to make you laugh—I hope!

Cilla appeared as just about everything—from an average housewife to a round-the-world yachtsman.

In real life, Cilla has a lot of different roles, too—she loves gardening, golfing, ski-ing, cooking and watching TV.

With thousands of fans all over the world, Cilla's come a long way from those early days in Liverpool, but stardom hasn't changed her. As she says herself: "I believe people will always think of me as the girl next door." And who could wish for a better neighbour than Cilla Black?

# MAKE YOUR OWN
## BIG'N'BERTHA

*Get Mum to help you copy these patterns—and make your favourite cartoon characters!*

**PLACE ON FOLD**

SEAM | CUFF RED CLOTH CUT 2 | SEAM
SEAM

**PLACE ON FOLD 2 (CENTRE OF FRONT AND BACK)**

NECK

BLOUSE
RED CLOTH
FOLD CLOTH IN FOUR AND
CUT FOR MAGYAR STYLE
BLOUSE

BODY

HEM

SEAM

PLACE ON FOLD 1

SLEEVE

SEAM

- - - GATHER - - -

**PLACE ON FOLD**

COLLAR RED CLOTH CUT 2

SEAM

SEAM | SEAM

HEM | HEM

TUNIC
BLACK CLOTH
CUT CENTRE OF BACK.
HEM EACH SIDE OF CUT AND ADD
SNAP FASTENERS. MAKE PLEAT
IN CENTRE OF FRONT SO THAT
WIDTH OF FRONT MEASURES
THE SAME AS FASTENED BACK.
CUT 2

SEAM | SEAM

HEM

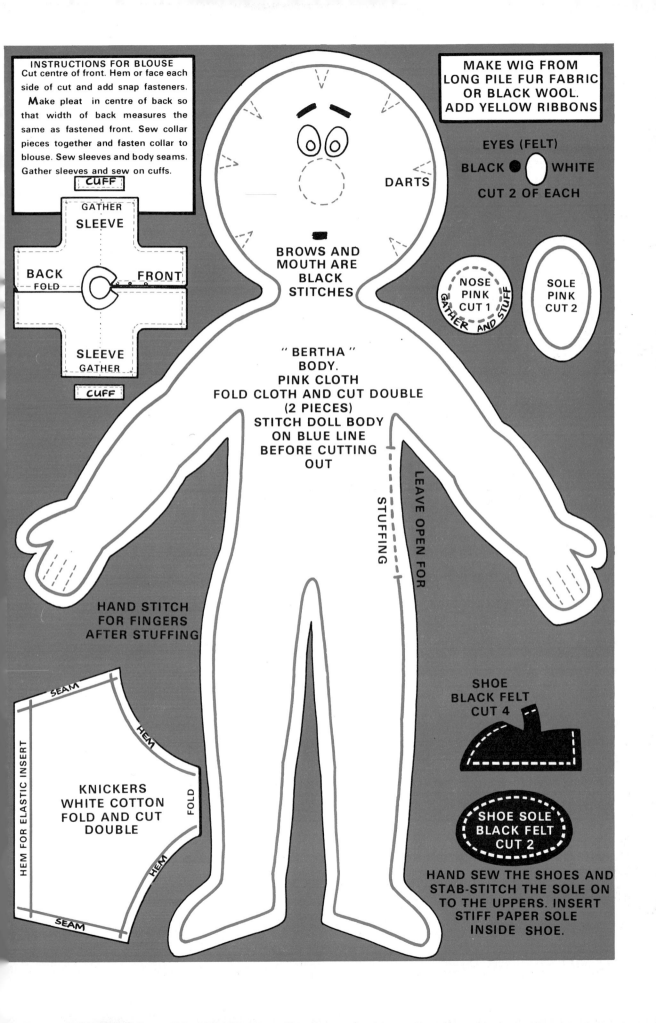

INSTRUCTIONS FOR BLOUSE
Cut centre of front. Hem or face each side of cut and add snap fasteners.
Make pleat in centre of back so that width of back measures the same as fastened front. Sew collar pieces together and fasten collar to blouse. Sew sleeves and body seams. Gather sleeves and sew on cuffs.

CUFF

GATHER
SLEEVE

BACK
FOLD

FRONT

SLEEVE
GATHER

CUFF

MAKE WIG FROM
LONG PILE FUR FABRIC
OR BLACK WOOL.
ADD YELLOW RIBBONS

EYES (FELT)
BLACK ● ○ WHITE
CUT 2 OF EACH

DARTS

BROWS AND
MOUTH ARE
BLACK
STITCHES

NOSE
PINK
CUT 1
GATHER AND STUFF

SOLE
PINK
CUT 2

"BERTHA"
BODY.
PINK CLOTH
FOLD CLOTH AND CUT DOUBLE
(2 PIECES)
STITCH DOLL BODY
ON BLUE LINE
BEFORE CUTTING
OUT

STUFFING

LEAVE OPEN FOR

HAND STITCH
FOR FINGERS
AFTER STUFFING

SHOE
BLACK FELT
CUT 4

SEAM

HEM

HEM FOR ELASTIC INSERT

KNICKERS
WHITE COTTON
FOLD AND CUT
DOUBLE

FOLD

HEM

SEAM

SHOE SOLE
BLACK FELT
CUT 2

HAND SEW THE SHOES AND
STAB-STITCH THE SOLE ON
TO THE UPPERS. INSERT
STIFF PAPER SOLE
INSIDE SHOE.

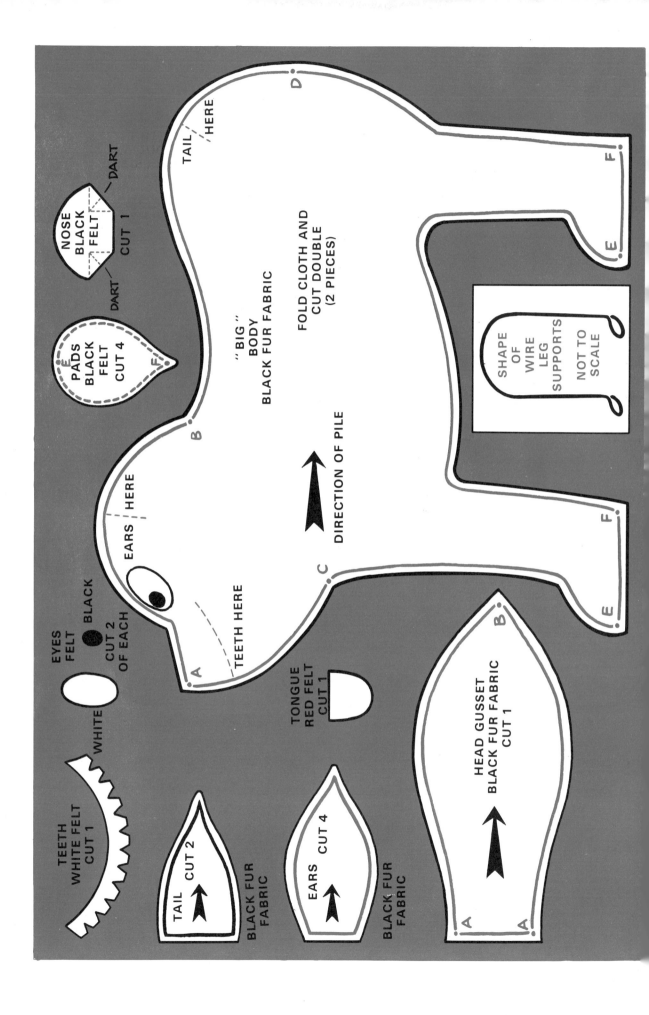

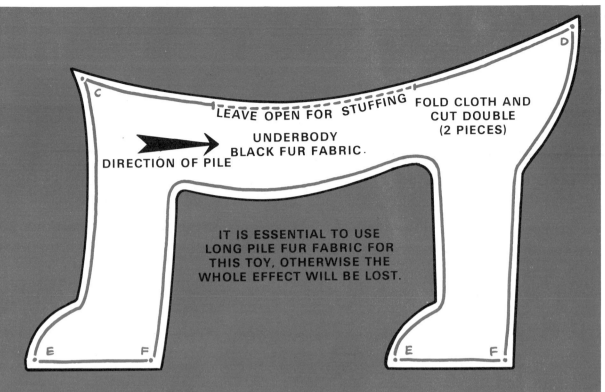

LEAVE OPEN FOR STUFFING

FOLD CLOTH AND CUT DOUBLE (2 PIECES)

UNDERBODY BLACK FUR FABRIC.

DIRECTION OF PILE

IT IS ESSENTIAL TO USE LONG PILE FUR FABRIC FOR THIS TOY, OTHERWISE THE WHOLE EFFECT WILL BE LOST.

## HOW TO MAKE UP "BIG"

Pin and tack the pieces together, matching A and B on the HEAD GUSSET to A and B on the head of main body pattern. Match C,D,E and F on underbody pieces to C,D, E and F on the main body pattern, leaving the feet open at the bottom for the felt pads to be sewn on later.

Use a long oversewing stitch for tacking, and tuck in the fur fabric pile as it is tacked, otherwise it will get caught up in the stitching when you machine it together.

Make wire supports for the legs, using enough wire to bend double for the feet.

Make sure you cover the felt well with padding to avoid the wire poking through the felt pads. Put the wire in when you start stuffing and stuff firmly all round it to make a firm leg. Sew the felt pads on the outside after stuffing the legs.

If you want to make a bigger version of Big or Bertha, get Mum to help you scale up these patterns.

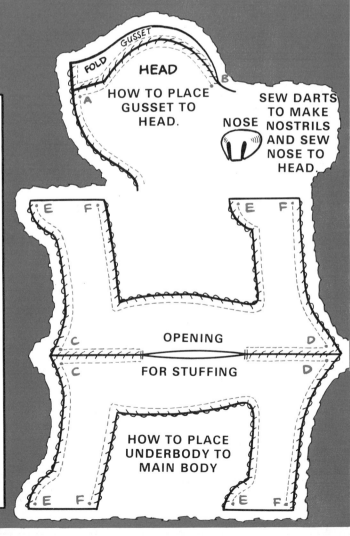

HEAD

HOW TO PLACE GUSSET TO HEAD.

SEW DARTS TO MAKE NOSTRILS AND SEW NOSE TO HEAD.

NOSE

OPENING FOR STUFFING

HOW TO PLACE UNDERBODY TO MAIN BODY

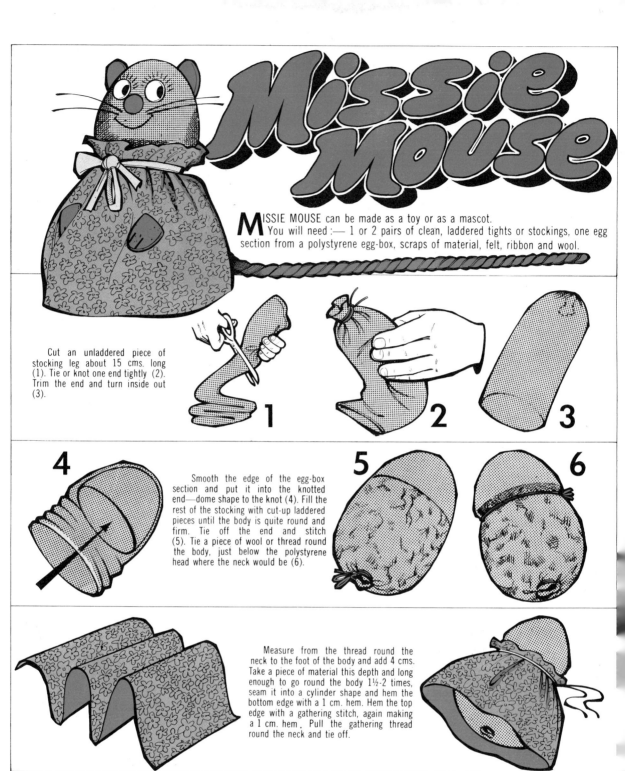

# Missie Mouse

**M**ISSIE MOUSE can be made as a toy or as a mascot.
You will need :— 1 or 2 pairs of clean, laddered tights or stockings, one egg section from a polystyrene egg-box, scraps of material, felt, ribbon and wool.

Cut an unladdered piece of stocking leg about 15 cms. long (1). Tie or knot one end tightly (2). Trim the end and turn inside out (3).

**1**

**2**

**3**

**4**

Smooth the edge of the egg-box section and put it into the knotted end—dome shape to the knot (4). Fill the rest of the stocking with cut-up laddered pieces until the body is quite round and firm. Tie off the end and stitch (5). Tie a piece of wool or thread round the body, just below the polystyrene head where the neck would be (6).

**5**

**6**

Measure from the thread round the neck to the foot of the body and add 4 cms. Take a piece of material this depth and long enough to go round the body 1½-2 times, seam it into a cylinder shape and hem the bottom edge with a 1 cm. hem. Hem the top edge with a gathering stitch, again making a 1 cm. hem. Pull the gathering thread round the neck and tie off.

Make a bow round the neck with a piece of ribbon or wool. Cut eyes, ears, nose, mouth and paws from felt and glue or stitch them in place. Glue or stitch paws to front of dress. You can, if you wish, embroider on the eyes, nose and mouth.

Make a long tail by crocheting some wool into a long chain or plait it and stitch to the back of the body.

Draw some strands of wool through the face for whiskers if Missie Mouse is to be a toy. Use some brush bristles if she is to be a mascot.

You can make Missie Mouse into a rabbit by cutting larger ears and, instead of stitching a long tail to the body, glue a blob of cotton-wool to the back of her dress.

# I'LL EAT MY HAT

Have you ever stopped to wonder why and where familiar sayings originated?

## AS MAD AS A HATTER

Hatters, before the Industrial Revolution, used mercury when making hats, unaware of its harmful properties.

As the dangerous metal was absorbed into their bodies, one of the first symptoms of sickness included mental aberrations —thus giving the well-known saying.

## LETTING THE CAT OUT OF THE BAG.

At country fairs in the Middle Ages, sucking pigs wrapped in sacks were sold.

But sometimes the poor purchaser arrived home to find he'd been tricked—and given a cat instead.

The only way to stop this deception was to open the sack at the fair—letting the cat out of the bag and exposing the cheat.

## WRONG SIDE OF THE BED.

Long ago, people actually believed that whichever side of the bed they got out of in the morning affected their behaviour for the rest of the day. Apparently the wrong side to them was the left side.

## GOD BLESS YOU

If you had sneezed in Ancient Greece, you would have been regarded as being in great personal danger.

The reason for this was probably because sneezing was thought to be the first symptom of plague.

Later, the Romans looked upon a sneeze as being an evil omen and the now well-known saying "God bless you" was a protection against evil spirits.

## I'LL EAT MY HAT

How many people know that the hat mentioned in this saying is not the millinery kind, but food? "Hattes" were made from eggs, veal, dates, saffron and salt. A somewhat strange concoction, don't you think?

## LAUGHING UP ONE'S SLEEVE

This phrase originated in the days when it was fashionable for men to wear very wide and long sleeves. This enabled them to hide any smiles on their faces by holding the sleeve in front of their faces.

# MIGHTY MIDGE

MIDGE WAS VERY FOND OF HER LITTLE BROTHER, HUMPHREY, AND TOOK GREAT CARE OF HIM.

REGAL CINEMA

Should be a super film, Humph. I'm sure we'll enjoy it.

JUST THEN—

Ha! Ha!

You—you brute!

WAAAAH!

A LITTLE LATER—

There he is! I'll soon fix him!

See how you like that!

REGAL CINEMA

I'll get my own back! I'll be waiting—you'll see!

Run, Humph! I'm going to call a gang meeting.

SOON—

Today's the last showing of "Cowboys Galore", so I'm counting on you to help us get in. Meet here with the gear in ten minutes, gang!

SOME TIME LATER—

They're bound to come back to see the picture, and I'll be waiting!

BUT—

A walking tepee! What's going on?

COWBOYS GALORE

By the time he's figured it out, me 'n' Humph'll be safely inside. It's one thing being a bully, but having brains is better!

# BIG SPENDER

**B**IG LIZ SPENDER of Summerfield was an amazing athlete. Unfortunately, her sporting ability vanished whenever she developed a crush on some boy. This gave sports captain, Jean Craig, big problems.

Finally, Graeme decided to concentrate on script-writing, too, and his medical knowledge came in handy when, with Bill, he wrote all the scripts for "Doctor at Large" and "Doctor in the House".

Fate seemed to keep the three of them together. When Tim and Graeme starred in "Broaden Your Mind", who turned up as guest star?

NO —no—it can't be!

Not him again!

Why fight it, fellas? We're just meant to be together.

And so, in 1970, Graeme, Bill and Tim joined forces as the Goodies.

THE GOODIES

Goody goody gumdrops . . .

And every year since then there's been a new series, each one funnier than the last.

And they've tangled with Kitten Kong, to say nothing of Dougal and Zebedee.

Time for bed.

They've appeared as racing demons at Le Mans . . . as Hell's Grannies . . . and as Mighty Mice . . .

Help!

There's a lot more to their tricks than meets the eye of the camera—elaborate set-ups like this are trimmed down so that all you see is Tim's helmet going up as Bill brings the hammer down.

Starting with a Decca album, "The World of the Goodies", which collected together background music for their TV shows, Graeme, Tim and Bill have recorded a whole load of hit songs, mainly written by Bill, on the Bradleys label, including "Nappy Love", "Funky Gibbon" and "Make a Daft Noise for Christmas", plus the New Goodies L.P.

# BIG 'n' BERTHA

BERTHA AND HER DOG, BIG, OFTEN FELL OUT WITH DAD. ONE DAY—

Hop it, you flea-bitten, feathered freaks! Leave my grass seed alone!

Poor Dad! I know how to help him.

LATER—

Tea's ready, Bertha!

Coming, Mum!

That should keep the birds away. It'll be a nice surprise for Dad.

THAT NIGHT—

I'll just check that I locked the garage before I go to bed.

AAH!

Oh, you found my surprise, then?

NEXT DAY—

This'll frighten the birds and no mistake!

SUDDENLY—

Hey, stop it, you stupid brute!

He's ruined it!

No wonder he attacked it! It's enough to frighten anybody with these awful clothes! Give it to me.

LATER—

It looks smarter now. We can't have the neighbours thinking we can't afford decent clothes for it.

My best suit! Oh, no!

Ringo Starr

# BOBBY DAZZLER

**B**OBBY DAZZLER was the only girl at Westbury Boarding School for Boys, where her mother was matron.

One morning at assembly, the headmaster had a special announcement to make.

BOBBY

Our school physician, Doctor Lane, has asked whether his daughter, Grace, may attend this school as a day-girl—and after serious consideration, I have agreed. After all, we already have one very successful girl pupil at Westbury.

A few minutes later—

Another girl at Westbury? Of all the stupid ideas! People will think we're cissies, or something!

Come off it, Mike! Several quite famous boys' schools are accepting girls, nowadays.

At break—

What do you suppose she'll be like, Don? Bet she has pigtails and a spotty nose!

And bandy legs!

Why not give the poor girl a chance? It's not her fault that her dad wants to send her to Westbury. She may be quite nice.

Two days later, Bobby was called to the Head's study.

I want you to meet our new pupil, Bobby.

This is hardly what the boys were expecting!

Grace won't be starting school until Monday—but I thought you'd like the chance to show her round today, Bobby.

Pleased to meet you, Grace!

But she doesn't look very pleased to meet me!

It's a wonder I haven't met you at the local youth club . . .

I wouldn't be seen dead at that place. How can you bear to wear that grisly uniform?

Oh, it's not that bad! This is our common room. We read and chat here in the evenings—and sometimes play records.

What a hideous shambles! Thank goodness I'm only going to be a day girl. At least I'll be able to get out of the place after school!

I'll show you the swimming pool now.

Don't bother! I loathe swimming. It simply ruins my hair.

This is getting somewhat heavy weather—to put it mildly!

At last it was time for Grace to leave—

Would you like to meet two of my friends before you go? They've just come out of class.

I'll meet them soon enough—unfortunately!

That can't be the new girl! She's stunning!

What a smasher! I can't wait till Monday! You were actually right to tell us to give her a chance, Bobby.

I wonder! Something tells me that Monday's going to be quite a day!

On Monday morning—

Let me carry your case . . .

No—let me! What a fantastic dress!

It seems like I'll be carrying my own things from now on! The Head will have a fit when he sees that dress. I wonder why she isn't wearing uniform.

At break—

Come to the tuck shop for a milk shake, Grace. My treat!

No, mine!

Milk shake? Ugh! Such a sickly, fattening drink!

I expect a sophisticated person like you prefers coffee, Grace?

I should think your tuck-shop coffee tastes quite revolting! Just take Bobby for one of your nasty milk shakes while I go and make-up my face!

Not very chatty, is she?

You can say that again! Still, maybe the poor girl's shy. She's certainly good-looking.

Grace caused another stir during maths.

Aah!

BANG!

What on earth?

It's a mechanical banger from the joke shop, sir. I must have set it off by accident.

As it's your first day, Grace, we'll overlook the matter this time— but kindly remember your manners in future!

That evening, when Grace had gone home—

First she sets off a banger in maths, then she falls asleep in history—there's something odd about Grace.

You wouldn't think anyone so beautiful could do such stupid things. Perhaps she's nervous.

Nervous my foot! There's more to it than that—but as yet I haven't guessed what!

The next morning—

Hello, Grace. Where's your pretty dress today?

That old fuddy-duddy of a headmaster telephoned my parents and said I was to wear these ghastly rags— and my father insisted! I feel a proper freak! Still, it won't be for long.

What does she mean?

During break—

Coming for a swim after school, Grace?

And ruin my hair style? You must be joking!

I hope you two boys are going to shower before your swim! The Headmaster's been complaining about mud getting into the pool. It costs a lot of money to clean and re-fill it, you know.

Would you girls go and get some notebooks for me from the school stationery room? Fetch the key from Mrs Dazzler and remember to return it afterwards.

OK, Mr Dudley.

In the stationery room—

You'd better take those to Mr Dudley right away, Bobby. He—er—seemed in a hurry. I'll lock up and take the key back to your mother.

I'm sure she's up to no good. Maybe I shouldn't leave her . . . oh, I'm not her watch-dog!

INK

After school—

I suppose I may as well watch you swim for a few minutes.

What's she up to now?

What's the Head looking so furious about?

Oh, no!

Ink! Some hooligan has poured ink into the pool! I'll find the culprit if it takes me all night! He will be expelled instantly!

Not "he"—me! I put the ink in the soppy little pool. Just another of my little jokes.

Later—

So Grace has been expelled. I can't say I'm sorry to see the back of her—for all her good looks.

I just don't understand it.

Don't you see? Grace didn't like Westbury any more than we liked her! She's been trying to get herself expelled ever since she arrived.

Next day—

Let me carry your books, Bobby.

Out of the way, Norton! I'm helping Bobby!

It hasn't taken those two long to let everything get back to normal!

**THE END**

# JUNIOR NANNY

Then Brian lost his balance.

You're a bit unlucky today! Up you come!

W-want to go home! It's nasty here!

Oh, there are lots of nice things about it. I'm going to buy you some candy floss, Brian. You'll like that.

I'll treat him, Chris.

It's nice! I'll give Eileen a bit.

Naughty donkey! It's MY candy floss!

Later— ...and now he won't stay on the beach, Matron.

Don't cry, Brian. You can stay here with me.

W-want Eileen!

Eileen will be along soon, Brian—at lunch-time.

Don't worry, Chris. He'll get over this by tomorrow.

I hope so, but... well, we'll see.

Next morning—

Easy now, Brian.

No! No! Nasty beach! Don't want to go down there!

It's no use, Nurse. Take him back and leave him with Anne. She's off-duty this morning, but that can't be helped.

Will you be all right, Brian?

Want you to stay with me, Eileen.

There's no need for you to miss the fun, Eileen. He'll have Nurse Anne and Colin to play with.

Want you to play with me!

All right, Brian. Don't cry.

If I make her go down to the beach now, she won't enjoy it. She's a kind little girl, and she really loves her brother.

Two days later—

Eileen is very good and patient with Brian. This isn't much of a holiday for her, though. It's much the same as being at home.

Poor kid—it's a shame. I'll try to keep Brian amused, and maybe Eileen will enjoy herself, too.

# on the

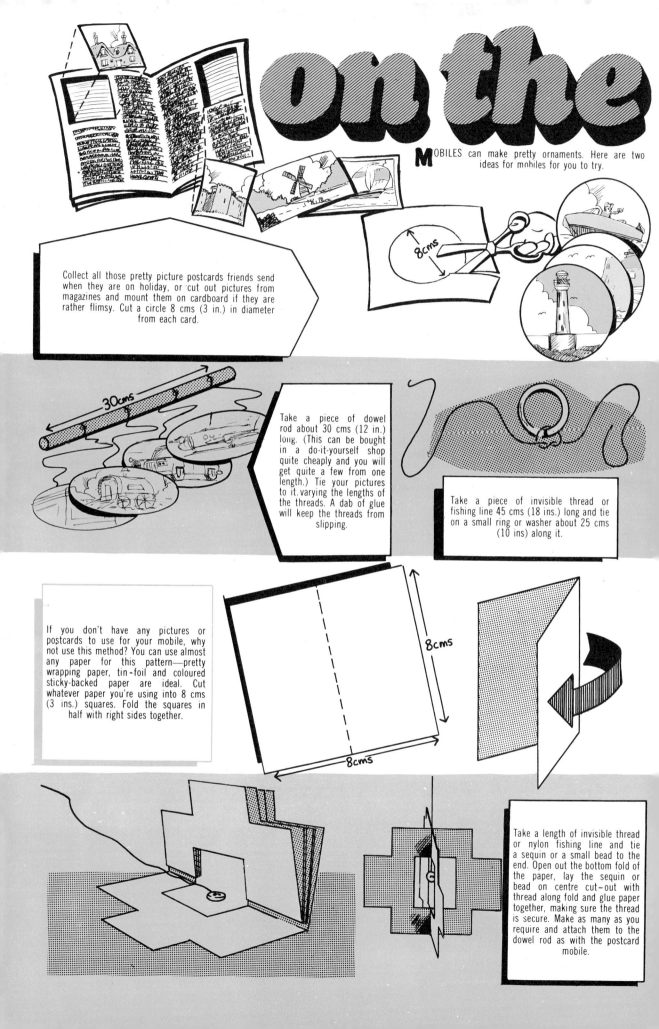

**M**OBILES can make pretty ornaments. Here are two ideas for mobiles for you to try.

Collect all those pretty picture postcards friends send when they are on holiday, or cut out pictures from magazines and mount them on cardboard if they are rather flimsy. Cut a circle 8 cms (3 in.) in diameter from each card.

Take a piece of dowel rod about 30 cms (12 in.) long. (This can be bought in a do-it-yourself shop quite cheaply and you will get quite a few from one length.) Tie your pictures to it, varying the lengths of the threads. A dab of glue will keep the threads from slipping.

Take a piece of invisible thread or fishing line 45 cms (18 ins.) long and tie on a small ring or washer about 25 cms (10 ins) along it.

If you don't have any pictures or postcards to use for your mobile, why not use this method? You can use almost any paper for this pattern—pretty wrapping paper, tin-foil and coloured sticky-backed paper are ideal. Cut whatever paper you're using into 8 cms (3 ins.) squares. Fold the squares in half with right sides together.

Take a length of invisible thread or nylon fishing line and tie a sequin or a small bead to the end. Open out the bottom fold of the paper, lay the sequin or bead on centre cut-out with thread along fold and glue paper together, making sure the thread is secure. Make as many as you require and attach them to the dowel rod as with the postcard mobile.

# move.

Glue two of these circles back to back enclosing the end of a length of invisible thread or nylon fishing line. Lay aside to set, preferably under a weight. Repeat with the others until you have the required number for your mobile. You can, if you wish, glue the circles together, then, when they have set, punch a small hole in the top of the circle and tie your card to your invisible thread or fishing line.

Tie the ends to the dowel rod with a dab of glue and there you have your mobile ready to be pinned to the ceiling.

Glue the bottom of one folded piece to the top of a second folded piece. Repeat twice so that you have four folded pieces glued to one another. Draw one of the designs given below* on to the top layer of the paper along the folded edge. Cut out the shaded areas carefully.

*

Experiment with different-sized starting squares; vary the number of folded pieces you use; design your own shapes; try using a variety of shapes on one mobile and use different colours of paper in one shape. These will all go to make more interesting mobiles.

# ODD *Girl* OUT

**T**HIS looked like being a really cheerful holiday, if the first couple of days were anything to go by. I sat in a hollow at the edge of the dunes and looked down to the sea; there were lovely, rolling waves, breaking and spreading across the flat sands.

The shouts and laughter of the people swimming and playing around in the water came to me on the light breeze, and I sighed longingly. How I envied them!

I hadn't really wanted to come away on holiday. I'd had a painful ear infection, and had felt pretty ghastly for a week or two, missing all the end-of-term excitement at school. The doctor's treatment soon had me crawling round again, but I felt so feeble that everything seemed to be too much trouble.

"Sue, love, you do look peaky,"
said Mum. "You ought to be picking up a bit now."

"She will do now, Mrs Lambert," said the doctor. "Take her away for a change of air, if you can. But no swimming or bathing, remember — not even with ear-plugs, young lady."

So Mum and Dad had booked up for a fortnight at this little seaside place that nobody had ever heard of, and here we were.

The Beckley Boarding House had been recommended by Aunt Doris.

"Always a nice crowd of people there, and lots of youngsters for Sue," she'd said. I had a look at them, that first day at lunch. There were a few elderly couples, and also several families with children in assorted sizes, and they all seemed to know one another.

There were four girls and two boys more or less in my age group, but one of them stood out from

all the rest, and was obviously a born leader. "Philip", they called him, and he was the taller of the two boys.

Philip always seemed to be organising things to do, and I desperately longed to be included in the plans. But, of course, he took no notice of me; though one of the girls did come across after the meal and say: "Hello, I'm Helen. Would you like to come swimming with us this afternoon?"

"She mustn't swim," said my mother straight away, before I could even open my mouth. (Have you noticed how mothers do that, as though you were a ventriloquist's dummy who couldn't speak up for yourself?)

Anyway, the girl just raised her eyebrows, said, "Sorry!" and turned away to join the others. Of course, Mum had to make it worse by saying in a voice that could be heard all over the

dining-room: "You'd better go up and have your rest now, Sue," and out we trooped, with me feeling about as big as a pin's head.

But at least the ear infection hadn't damaged my hearing, because I heard another girl — the one they called Mary — say: "Mummy's girl mustn't go near the water. Mummy's girl must have her little nap." The others said, "Shhh!" but they laughed just the same.

The afternoon brought the excitement of a walk along the prom to the pier and back with Mum and Dad; a thrilling tea in a cafe; a stupendous visit to the park to watch old men playing bowls and then supper and early bed.

The next day was almost a repeat, except that we had two rounds of miniature golf in the morning, and then the prom walk in the afternoon again. Mum and Dad kept on talking brightly and all the time I was thinking how wonderful it would be to be down there in the water, with Philip chasing me with the beach ball, and splashing me instead of Mary. I seemed the odd girl out among all the other youngsters.

"That's a fine-looking lad," said my father from our seat on the prom. "Well built. Swims well, too."

I pretended I didn't know which one he was talking about, and said: "Oh, do you think so?"

I must have sounded so bored stiff (which I was, let's face it) that Mum and Dad were quite relieved next morning when I said I'd rather take a book out on the dunes while they went on a shopping expedition.

**S**O, I ambled down to the dunes and found a comfortable spot, but it was just my luck that the gang from the boarding-house chose that way down to the beach. I hoped they would go by without noticing me, but they stopped. It was Helen again who spoke.

"Hello, Sue. Would you like to come out with us this afternoon, over to the next bay?"

I was ready to smile and accept when Mary stepped forward.

"Don't be silly, Helen. You know Mummy wouldn't let her. Little Susie mustn't tire herself." Then she spoke directly to me. "Can't think how you put up with that mother of yours, telling you what to do all the time. You wouldn't catch me letting my mother boss me like that! And why on earth do you go trailing around with your parents, looking like three dismal day-trippers? I'm always expecting your father to roll up his trousers like a funny postcard and go paddling with his corns!"

Mary was obviously the witty one, and some of the others duti-fully laughed. But as for me — well, I know I say some pretty awful things about my parents, but I only say them to myself when I'm fed-up. And nobody else is going to criticise them while I've got a tongue in my head.

"Don't you dare talk about my parents like that!" I blurted out furiously, jumping up in a flurry of dry sand. "They had to break into their savings to bring me away for this holiday because I've been ill. And if they look like day-trippers, then day-trippers are the best kind of people to be, and I wouldn't swop them for all the tea in China!"

"Dear, dear!" mocked Mary. "Now Susie's getting naughty and cross!"

"Come on, Mary!" called Philip. "I want my swim."

They all ran off, leaving me, lonely and miserable, wishing I hadn't lost my temper, and knowing that even that nice Helen wouldn't try to make friends again after my outburst. So there I was, with only a solitary seagull to speak to.

Suddenly I heard a voice.

"Do you mind if I sit down?" It was a boy's voice, and for a moment my heart thumped — had Philip come back on his own? But it wasn't Philip. The boy who was standing awkwardly behind me was "the other one," as I had thought of him. Not that I had thought of him much; he was always quiet, and I hardly noticed him when Philip was around. I was so disappointed that I was barely polite.

"Help yourself," I said, and he slithered down to sit beside me. There was a long silence.

"Thought I'd come back, as you're on your own," he said at last. I was watching Philip chasing Helen with a long strand of seaweed, and hardly heard him. "If you'd rather be alone, I'll go," said the boy, half rising.

"Stay if you want to," I said grudgingly, and he lowered himself again. Philip had caught Helen and was carrying her back into the water. He looked so strong and fair, and they were all having such fun, that I sighed heavily. The boy beside me took off his glasses, handed them to me, and then solemnly got up, did a handstand right in front of me, waving his legs in the air, and then collapsed in a heap. He looked so funny that I involuntarily smiled.

"That's better," he said. "You look nice when you smile."

"What on earth did you do that for?" I asked.

"Had to do something to make you notice me, hadn't I?" He put his glasses back on and started running his fingers through a thatch of mouse-brown hair, scattering sand in all directions. "We can't all do the Mr Universe bit to show off our muscles," he said, "but I'm quite nice when you get to know me."

He gave me such a friendly grin that I couldn't help returning it. "I know you're Sue," he went on, "and I'm Ian, so now we're introduced." He began to look serious. "I had to come back, actually, to apologise for Mary, because she'll never do it for herself. She may be my cousin, but I wouldn't like you to think we're all as ill-mannered as

she is. Want a bit of chocolate?"

He took a bar out of his pocket, and soon we were munching happily. Then I told him why I wasn't allowed to swim, and he said: "Fair enough. I'm not too keen on water myself. What say we go for a walk along the cliffs?"

"No, thanks," I said. "I like it here, watching people."

"For 'people' I take it you mean Philip?" he said, and I couldn't tell if he was hurt or amused. In any case, I had to take my chance.

"Please tell me about him," I begged. "He never looks at me, let alone speaks to me."

Ian looked as though he was about to say something, then checked himself and looked at me closely. His clear grey eyes were warm and friendly behind the glasses.

"He's my cousin, too, you

know," he said. "He's Mary's brother, in fact. Tell you what, I'll arrange for you to speak to him yourself, tonight after supper. Wait behind when your parents go to the lounge for coffee."

He got up then, and ran to join the others. For a moment, I was sorry he'd gone; but then I began to think about Philip again, and soon forgot Ian. I rehearsed all the things I would say to Philip that night, and spent the rest of the day in a kind of blissful haze.

I took more care than usual with my appearance when we went down to supper, and Mum was pleased.

"Sue's looking better already, isn't she, Dad?" she said.

Afterwards, when we were leaving the dining-room, I hung back, and they went on. Mary and the rest of the gang began to leave, laughing, and ignoring me, but Ian nodded to me over their heads, and called Philip back.

He whispered something to him, but Philip, who must have known I was standing in the doorway, said out loud: "Stop and speak to Spineless Sue? No thanks, mate. Wouldn't be seen dead talking to her or her grotty parents. You've got a nerve, suggesting it!"

I didn't wait for more. On tiptoe I raced to the lounge, and then sauntered in to join Mum and Dad.

"Hello, love," said Dad. "What about a game of Scrabble?"

"Come and have your coffee first, dear," said Mum. "Why, you've got quite a colour! I knew this place would do you good."

Dear old Mum and Dad. How dare that rude boy call them 'grotty'?

"Yes, I'd like to play," I told Dad, and I smiled and smiled, though I had never felt less like it. For I knew what I'd done. I had thrown away the chance of friendship with Ian, who was worth ten of his good-looking and thoroughly unpleasant cousin. Dad got out the Scrabble board.

A quiet voice said: "Mind if I play, too, Mr Lambert? Sue and I will take on the two of you."

Ian smiled at me as he sat down beside Mum on the settee.

"That'll be nice, son," said Dad. I nodded agreement, and now my smile was the real thing. I wasn't going to be the odd girl out any longer.

**THE END.**

**4** These signs have all been jumbled up. Can you make out what they are pointing to?

**5** At first glance these two pictures of a chimps' tea party look identical, but if you look more closely you will see six differences.

**6** We asked our artist to draw a variety of animals and this is what he drew for us! What different animals make up this weird creature?

**7** How many of the birds in the aviary do you recognise?

**8** There are ten articles hidden in this drawing. Can you find them all?

# Janet On Wheels

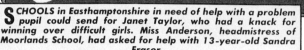

SCHOOLS in Easthamptonshire in need of help with a problem pupil could send for Janet Taylor, who had a knack for winning over difficult girls. Miss Anderson, headmistress of Moorlands School, had asked for help with 13-year-old Sandra Fraser.

Sandra certainly seems to resent discipline, Miss Anderson.

I expect a reasonable standard of behaviour, Miss Taylor, but Sandra demands an unreasonable degree of freedom.

She's cheeky, wild and a nuisance in class. My staff and I are at the end of our tether.

May I see Sandra, now?

Sandra's class was having a cookery lesson.

That's Sandra over there. I'll ask Miss Watts to excuse her. Would you like to use my office to speak to her?

If it's OK with Miss Watts, I'll chat with Sandra in here.

She'll probably give you a load of cheek. I put her over there to work by herself because she was being a nuisance.

She's banging away at that pastry as if it was an enemy! Ah, well, here goes.

Hi, Sandra. I'm Janet Taylor. I expect you know why I'm here?

I know! You're supposed to sort me out. Well, it's not on, so clear off before I lose my temper.

Am I supposed to be scared?

I warned you!

Sandra! Oh, you dreadful girl!

I'm so sorry, Miss Taylor! I'll report Sandra to Miss Anderson for this dreadful behaviour.

There's no need for that. This is between Sandra and me

Oh, my goodness!

And that's the end of that little incident. Now I need to wash my face.

I'll show you to the cloakroom. I need to wash my face now, too!

You put too much water in your pastry, Sandra. It was too sticky!

She's wild but she has a sense of fair play.

She's not a bit like I expected her to be.

Teachers aren't supposed to do things like that to pupils.

I know—but I'm not a teacher. Let's walk, and I'll tell you about my job.

It must be great to be always on the move. One of the reasons I don't like school is because there's too much sitting around.

How about PE? Games? Don't you like them?

They'd be all right if there weren't so many rules. Rules annoy me. I think I'll skip school this afternoon.

How about me keeping you company? We could go for a ride on my scooter, if I can get a crash helmet for you.

That afternoon—

It's a rough neighbourhood and Mrs Fraser says Sandra has become involved with a wild crowd. It'll take something special to get her away from them.

A few days later—

You've been observing Sandra in and out of the classroom for the past few days. Have you reached any conclusions, Janet?

She's no great learner, that's for sure. But I think she'd behave better in class if she had an outlet for her physical energy.

# THE ISLAND OF SECRETS

**T**WO thousand miles off the coast of Chile lies one of the most isolated places in the world—Easter Island. Discovery by the Dutchman Roggeveen on Easter Sunday in 1722 revealed one of the world's strangest mysteries—the stone statues of Easter Island. Why were these massive statues carved and how were they transported across the island to their shrines known as "ahus"? And why did the work stop so abruptly?

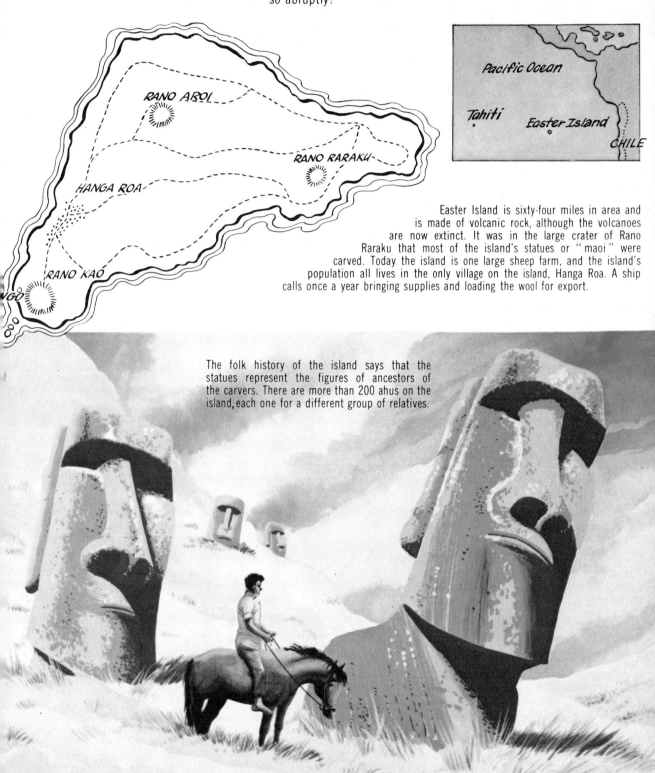

Easter Island is sixty-four miles in area and is made of volcanic rock, although the volcanoes are now extinct. It was in the large crater of Rano Raraku that most of the island's statues or "maoi" were carved. Today the island is one large sheep farm, and the island's population all lives in the only village on the island, Hanga Roa. A ship calls once a year bringing supplies and loading the wool for export.

The folk history of the island says that the statues represent the figures of ancestors of the carvers. There are more than 200 ahus on the island, each one for a different group of relatives.

The carving was done with basalt pick-axes, which still lie scattered around the unfinished and finished statues which never made the journey to the ahus. Archaeologists say they might one day discover why the carving stopped so suddenly, but as yet the mystery remains unsolved.

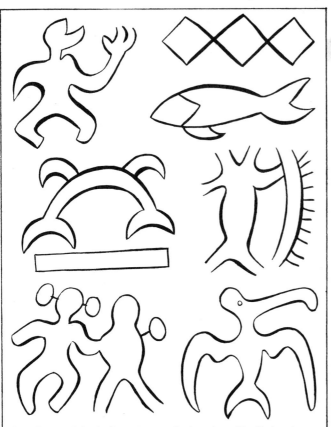

The Easter Island "rongo-rongo" boards with their strange hieroglyphics remain another mystery. The symbols (some of which are shown above) have so far remained undeciphered. The priests of the last century took the knowledge of the boards with them when they died.

The ancient dwellings were built in the shape of a longboat. Wo poles were fitted into the holes in the stones, arched over, covered with thatch.

A strange, religious "birdman" cult was practis at the deserted village of Orongo. In this area the island, the rocks are covered with numer carvings representing birdmen and their god. T illustration shows one such carving.

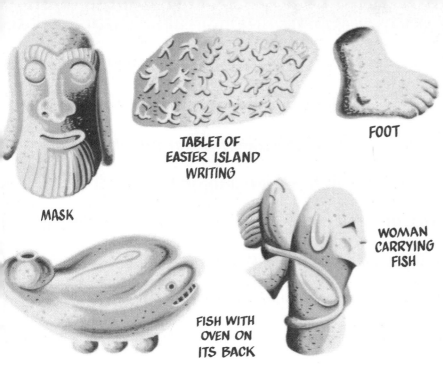

MASK

TABLET OF
EASTER ISLAND
WRITING

FOOT

WOMAN
CARRYING
FISH

FISH WITH
OVEN ON
ITS BACK

These illustrations show some of the stone carvings which were found in underground caves. A shortage of wood on the island led to the volcanic rock being used. Today, the natives copy these carvings for the tourists.

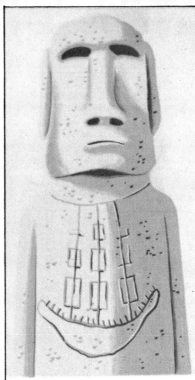

During excavations at Rano Raraku, this statue was found to have a three-masted sailing ship carved on its chest.

These statues stand almost forty feet high, but are now almost buried by three centuries of erosion. Many of the figures were eventually toppled and almost destroyed, though no one knows why. The statues keep their secrets.

# LOTS OF BOXES

**W**E all get presents in boxes or fancy jars at some time or other, and it seems such a shame to throw them out, when, with a bit of thought and time spent on them, they can be used again for giving presents or storing odds and ends. Here are a few ideas for giving them a new lease of life.

A plain, flat box can be transformed by carefully covering the lid with self-coloured metallic paper. A bow or a piece of toning ribbon will add a finishing touch. To make it look extra special, glue some beads or sequins to the paper.

A wooden box, or one which is fairly rigid, can be decorated with shells gathered from the beach. Make sure the shells are thoroughly clean and dry. Glue a piece of felt to the lid of the box. Arrange your shells into a pattern then glue them individually in place. If you wish, you can give the shells and the box a coat of clear polyurethane sealer to make them shine.

Shoe boxes and paper-tissue boxes can be turned into a useful storage container for newspaper cuttings, sewing odds and ends, or any other collection you may have. You can cover the box with a scrap of material as if you were wrapping a parcel (treat the box and lid separately) cutting excess fabric from the corners to keep down the bulk and using adhesive suitable for material. Make sure the edges are neat.

Sticky-backed, waterproof shelf covering can also be used.

You can also use stamps or pictures cut from magazines, and stick these on the box in a collage, sealing the finished box with a coat of polyurethane sealer. Autumn leaves can also be used, but make sure they are clean and dry. Seal with a coat of polyurethane sealer.

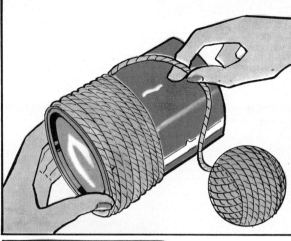

An old coffee tin, or drinking chocolate tin, can be made into a handy container. Remove the label from the tin and wash it thoroughly. To make sure it's really dry, put it in the oven AFTER Mum has finished baking and the oven is switched OFF.

When the tin is cool and dry, take some seam binding, or ribbon, or chunky wool or string, and wind it around the tin, gluing it carefully. The ends can be neatly tucked in at the top and bottom.

Or try using some of those coloured fancy labels you can buy in stationers'. Stick them on at random to give a pretty look to your tin. Give them a clear polyurethane varnish to stop them from becoming unstuck.

Pretty and unusual shaped jars can be used again to give as a gift, filled with bath salts, or sweets, or cotton-wool balls and a hundred and one other things.

Wash and dry the jars thoroughly, removing all labels. Paint the jars with a tin of enamel—there are lots of colours to choose from and they can be bought in any craft shop.

Fill your jar, tie a bow of ribbon round the neck and there you have an attractive gift. If you think the jar looks too plain, add a few sticky labels as before, or buy some Letraset shapes, or transfers, to put on it.

These are just a few ideas of how to renovate boxes and jars, so get out your scraps and go!

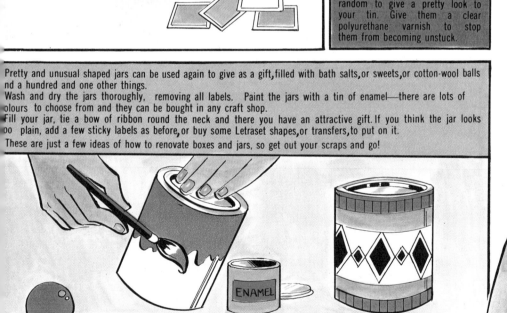

ENAMEL

FOURTEEN-YEAR-OLD Moira Davies had a magic mirror. Anything it was directed upon became invisible for a time. One day, during school holidays.....

# MOIRA'S MAGIC MIRROR

PART-TIME FRUIT PICKERS WANTED

Oh, look, Joan, a chance to earn a bit of extra pocket-money!

Let's go in and apply, Moira.

Farmer Jones was only too pleased to take them on.

Come along with me, girls, and I'll show you where to start picking.

You two can work this row. As you fill a container, take it back to be weighed so that we know how much to pay you.

That sounds simple enough. Come on, Joan, let's get started.

Later—

Well, look here, Jake! Two lovely, full containers! And all for us, eh?

'Ere, let us 'elp you with them. Don't want you two ladies fallin' off the ladders, do we?

Well, thank you. They are a bit heavy!

OK, scarper!

Hey, come back with our apples!

Well, of all the nerve! C'mon! Let's tell Farmer Jones!

We couldn't prove anything, Joan. Let's just start all over again. At least we'll know to be more careful next time.

Later—

Well, that's mine filled again, but I'm scared to go to the checkpoint in case we run into those boys again!

Tell you what—you stay here while I go and see if they're hanging around anywhere.

There they are!

Soon as we've filled these two, we'll go back to those girls and pinch their next lot!

Sure, that way we can get double pay without flogging ourselves to death. It's money for old rope!

That's what they think! I'll soon put a stop to their little game. First I get my mirror into focus . . .

Help! The bottom of my ladder's disappeared!

So's mine! Jump for it!

Aaaaaagh!

What on earth are you two playing at? Just look at all the fruit you've wasted!

It wasn't our fault, mister. It's those rotten ladders o' yours! The bottom halves disappeared!

But the ladders were complete again.

Disappeared, eh? You young hooligans! D'you take me for an idiot? Now, get back up there and pick!

Now to make all the apples disappear!

Wait a minute. Where are all the apples gone off this tree?

Well—er—we spilled a few, b-but we did fill a couple of containers— look!

Quick, mirror, make them seem empty!

B-but they're empty . . .

Just as I thought! You've been eating instead of picking!

If I get my hands on you, I'll—I'll . . .

Thanks, mirror. They won't be bothering us again!

What happened, Moira? And why did the toughs leave these two full containers?

Oh, to make up for the ones they stole, I expect. We'll assume that, anyway. It'd be a pity to waste them, wouldn't it?

DOTTIE SIGNS

ZOO

JAIL

CACTUS PLANTS

GUN SHOP

INDIAN RESERVATION

AUSTRALIA

BUTCHER'S

PLUMBER

FENCING SCHOOL

**VAL MARTIN** was the relief District Nurse for the Storrhurst area. One morning, at her cottage—

WHAT HAPPENED THIS TIME, MRS BRETT? IF YOU GO INTO THE KITCHEN, RODDY, YOU CAN TAKE A CHOCOLATE BISCUIT FROM THE BLUE TIN ON THE SHELF.

IT WASN'T RODDY'S FAULT, NURSE. IT WAS BRIAN RICKETTS WHO STARTED THE FIGHT.

MRS BRETT, WHEN IS YOUR FAMILY GOING TO GIVE UP FEUDING WITH THE RICKETTS?

THE FEUD WAS NONE OF OUR STARTING, NURSE. JIM RICKETTS SHOT DANNY, THE BEST SHEEPDOG MY HUSBAND EVER HAD. ABOUT A YEAR AGO, IT WAS, JUST BEFORE CHRISTMAS. JIM TRIED TO MAKE OUT IT WAS A MISTAKE, SAYING HE MISTOOK DANNY FOR A FOX.

BUT ISN'T THAT LIKELY?

NO. JIM HAD A SHEEPDOG, TOO, WHICH ALWAYS JUST MISSED WINNING COMPETITIONS BECAUSE OF DANNY. MY HUSBAND ASKED HIM STRAIGHT OUT IF HE'D KILLED DANNY DELIBERATELY AND HE DIDN'T DENY IT.

I HEARD THAT JIM AND YOUR HUSBAND WERE THE BEST OF FRIENDS BEFORE ALL THIS. PERHAPS JIM WAS TOO PROUD TO ANSWER AN ACCUSATION THAT HE FELT SHOULD NEVER HAVE BEEN MADE BETWEEN TWO FRIENDS.

WE DON'T SEE IT THAT WAY, NURSE. COME ALONG, RODDY. I'VE SOME SHOPPING TO DO BEFORE WE GO HOME.

Next morning—

HELLO, VICAR. IT LOOKS LIKE, BETWEEN US, WE'RE GOING TO FILL THAT POST-BOX WITH CHRISTMAS CARDS. I'M GOING TO REALLY ENJOY MYSELF THIS CHRISTMAS. I'M DECORATING THE COTTAGE AND GETTING A CHRISTMAS TREE. AND I'M HAVING SIX CHILDREN FROM THE DALE HOME WITH ME FOR THE DAY.

GOOD FOR YOU. COLONEL KENNARD TELLS ME HE GAVE YOU THE PICK OF THE TREES IN HIS WOOD AND YOU CHOSE WHAT YOU CALLED A 'FRIENDLY ONE'.

IT'S CHUBBY AND BRIGHT-LOOKING, AND I FELT IT WAS A TREE THAT WOULD BRING HAPPINESS.

YOU'RE A VERY WARM-HEARTED YOUNG PERSON, NURSE. I THINK THAT'S WHY YOU ARE SO LIKED IN THE VALLEY. BY THE WAY, DON'T FORGET YOU'RE JUDGING THE CHRISTMAS CAKES AT THE WOMEN'S INSTITUTE MEETING TOMORROW.

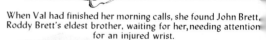

When Val had finished her morning calls, she found John Brett, Roddy Brett's eldest brother, waiting for her, needing attention for an injured wrist.

IT'S A SPRAIN, JOHN. HOW DID IT HAPPEN?

A FIGHT WITH MIKE RICKETTS. I FOUND HIM SNOOPING NEAR OUR PRIZE SHEEP AND TOLD HIM TO GET OFF OUR LAND AND— WELL, IT CAME TO BLOWS.

THIS IS THE SEASON OF GOODWILL, JOHN. PERHAPS IF YOU COULD MAKE FRIENDS WITH MIKE IT WOULD SET THE SCENE FOR YOUR FAMILIES MAKING THINGS UP.

MIKE AND I WERE FRIENDS ONCE, BUT THAT'S PAST NOW. HE'S A RICKETTS AND I'M A BRETT.

The following afternoon, at the Village Hall—

IT'S DIFFICULT TO DECIDE WHICH IS BEST. I SAY IT'S BETWEEN THESE TWO.

THESE TWO CAKES WERE MADE BY MRS RICKETTS AND MRS BRETT. THEY COULD ALWAYS SHARE THE PRIZE.

IT'S A TURKEY. THEY CAN HARDLY CHOP IT IN TWO!

I'M NOT QUITE SURE HOW YOU CAN SHARE IT, BUT MY SUGGESTION IS THAT YOU GET TOGETHER TO COOK IT. THEN BOTH FAMILIES CAN ENJOY EATING IT TOGETHER.

LET HER HAVE IT. THE WAY HER HUSBAND RUNS HIS FARM, SHE'S MORE IN NEED OF A TURKEY THAN I AM!

Mrs Ricketts left the hall. When the meeting had finished—

HOW'S YOUR LITTLE HAPPINESS TREE? HAS IT BEEN FELLED YET?

I'M GOING TO COLLECT IT ON CHRISTMAS EVE. RALPH—ONE OF MY FIRST-AIDERS—IS GOING TO HELP ME. JOE PARSONS IS LENDING ME ONE OF HIS TRUCKS.

On Christmas Eve—

WITH ALL THE RAIN WE'VE HAD, THERE'S A CHANCE OF FLOODING ON THE ROADS—ESPECIALLY NEAR THE WOODS. SO GO CAREFULLY, NURSE.

I'LL BE CAREFUL, JOE. 'BYE.

HEARD THE LATEST, NURSE VAL? MR BRETT'S PRIZE SHEEP HAS DISAPPEARED, AND HE SAYS MR RICKETTS HAS STOLEN IT. MR BRETT SAYS THAT IF THE SHEEP ISN'T RETURNED BY FOUR O'CLOCK, HE'S GOING OVER TO THE RICKETTS' FARM FOR A SHOWDOWN.

OH, NO! THAT'S TERRIBLE! WE MUST HURRY AND GET MY TREE, RALPH, THEN I'LL CALL ON MR BRETT AND SEE IF I CAN REASON WITH HIM.

When they had collected the tree—

I'VE NEVER SEEN THAT STREAM SO HIGH AND FLOWING SO FAST! I WOULDN'T LIKE TO FALL IN THERE!

NEITHER WOULD I, RALPH. LOOK OVER THERE. SOMETHING'S CAUGHT UP IN THE BRUSHWOOD. IT'S A SHEEP!

I'M SURE THAT'S FARMER BRETT'S SHEEP. IT MUST HAVE WANDERED AWAY AND BECOME TRAPPED. THE SWELL IS GRADUALLY LOOSENING THAT BRUSHWOOD—IT'LL BE SWEPT AWAY.

IF I TURN THE TRUCK SO THAT WE CAN TOPPLE THE TREE ACROSS THE WATER, I'LL BE ABLE TO EASE MYSELF ALONG IT TO GET TO THE SHEEP.

Val reached the young sheep and got a strong hold on it.

GOT IT! NOW TO INCH MY WAY BACK.

Val edged her way along again, pulling the sheep with her, every second seeming like an hour. Then—

YOU'RE AS WHITE AS A SHEET, NURSE VAL. YOU NEARLY WENT IN A COUPLE OF TIMES.

DON'T I KNOW IT! RIGHT, LET'S GET THIS SHEEP INTO THE TRUCK.

THE END.

# SILLY SAYINGS

# SCHOOLGIRL VET

KAY BURROWS hoped one day to qualify as an animal nurse or even become a vet like her brother, David. One Saturday morning at breakfast—

By the way, David, I wanted to ask you if—

Sorry, Kay. Must dash. It's the lambing season and we're rushed off our feet. Don't expect me home until late, Mum.

Really, Kay! There may be some excuse for David, but there's no need for YOU to gobble your breakfast as if you haven't a minute to spare!

But there is, Mum. I'm due at the Moorside Riding Stables in half an hour. Some of us volunteered to help handicapped children learn to ride.

On her way to the stables—

I must say, you have an easy life, don't you? Whenever I pass you're just standing here, growing fatter.

Candy is a strong pony, Kay, and needs a firm hand to control him. You couldn't expect a disabled child to manage him.

Of course not, Mum. Mr Morton has rounded up some quiet ones specially for the kids to ride.

At the stables—

I've got plenty of hacks, but they're rather big. We need more beginners' ponies . . . small and placid.

My brother must know of some. But he's so busy just now, I haven't had a chance to talk to him.

# "I Wish I Were You!"

ONE day, Katie Munn and Pat Tiler were sitting in the park having one of their moaning sessions.

The trouble is, Pat, when you're the eldest, you get all sorts of jobs to do. And you get the blame for the things the younger ones get up to—like I will if Kevin gets his jeans torn climbing that tree.

It's no fun being the youngest in the family! Mum and Dad treat me as if I was still a baby. Jean, my sister, orders me about as if I was her personal servant and Mark, my brother, never takes me seriously.

Tessa, don't throw the ball in the flower bed!

I wish I had someone to tell off like that. I'm always at the other end of a telling-off in our house.

We should do a swop! I'll try to mend your shirt without Mum seeing it, Kevin. Come on, Tessa. I'll see you later, Pat.

That's the difference between you and me. Nobody thinks I can do anything. Well, see you later. 'Bye.

When Katie reached home, Mrs Tiler was there, too.

What a help you are with the little ones, Katie. It would do Pat good to change places with you some time.

Actually, Pat was saying this afternoon that she'd like a bit more responsibility.

I sometimes think I ask too much of Katie. What about letting them change places for a day?

What a good idea! I'll tell Pat when I get home. I'll send her round at seven-thirty tomorrow morning.

Next morning, at seven-thirty—

Come along, rise and shine, you lazy lot!

Don't make so much noise, Pat. I'm having another half an hour in bed. You see to Tessa. I'll see you tonight.

May I help?

Not at all, Katie. This is your day off— just go through to the sitting-room.

Mum, did I leave a pair of tights down there?

Later, when Katie arrived at the Tilers' house—

There's a pair here. Shall I bring them up?

No, don't touch them! I don't want them all snagged. Sorry, Katie, but Pat said you were to be treated as one of the family.

When breakfast was ready —

Is tea OK, Katie? Or would you prefer coffee? How about another piece of toast?

Everything's fine, thanks.

They do make a fuss about everything!

'Bye! See you at tea-time.

'Morning all!

It's like Piccadilly Circus in the rush hour in here!

After breakfast—

"I'll do the breakfast dishes."

"No, Katie. You've no chores today. Go up to Pat's room and amuse yourself."

"At last—something to do. After I've tidied this, I'll see if Pat has any new records."

"It's only ten o'clock. What am I going to do? I wonder how Pat's getting on."

"Please, Mrs Tiler, aren't there any jobs I can do? Are you needing any shopping done?"

"I always do the shopping myself, thanks. Why not have a walk in the garden?"

Later—

"Mr Tiler usually does the garden, Katie. Are you sure these are weeds? Anyway, lunch is ready."

"I wish I'd left the weeds to grow! Never mind, maybe Mark will be in to lunch."

He was. After lunch—

"Well, I'm doing the washing-up. You go and put your feet up for half an hour."

"But that's not in the bargain."

"Katie's right, Mum. I'll help her with the dishes."

"Enjoying your day of leisure? Or are you as bored stiff as you look?"

"I'm not used to having nothing to do and it's not the treat I thought it would be."

"You feel you're wasting time doing nothing? Well, let's finish these dishes and we'll go out for the afternoon, shall we?"

"Well—er—thanks, Mark, I'd like that."

"This is a better way to spend time than sitting about doing nothing. And Mark's great company."

That evening, when Mark walked Katie home—

"I wonder how Pat's coped today with your lot?"

"I don't know, but please try to treat her more as an equal in future, Mark, and not just as your little sister."

"We've missed you, Katie."

"I'm exhausted! It's back to you, Katie, with the best of luck!"

"I wouldn't swop with Pat for anything. She's may be Mark's sister, but I'm the one who's going out with him tomorrow!"

# NEW HOBBIES from OLD SKILLS

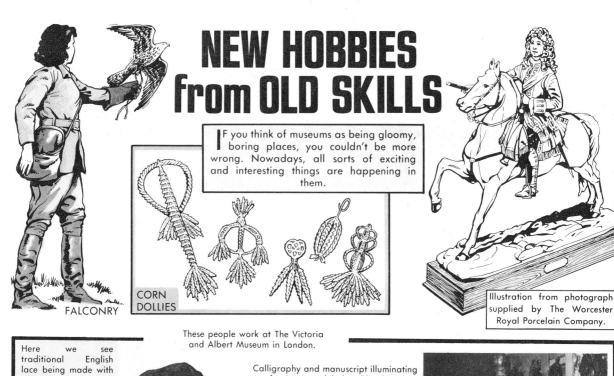

**IF** you think of museums as being gloomy, boring places, you couldn't be more wrong. Nowadays, all sorts of exciting and interesting things are happening in them.

CORN DOLLIES

FALCONRY

Illustration from photograph supplied by The Worcester Royal Porcelain Company.

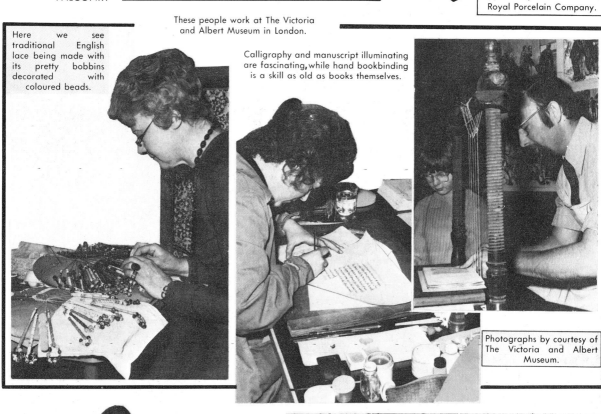

These people work at The Victoria and Albert Museum in London.

Here we see traditional English lace being made with its pretty bobbins decorated with coloured beads.

Calligraphy and manuscript illuminating are fascinating, while hand bookbinding is a skill as old as books themselves.

Photographs by courtesy of The Victoria and Albert Museum.

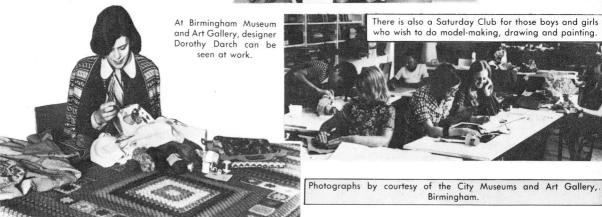

At Birmingham Museum and Art Gallery, designer Dorothy Darch can be seen at work.

There is also a Saturday Club for those boys and girls who wish to do model-making, drawing and painting.

Photographs by courtesy of the City Museums and Art Gallery, Birmingham.

At the National Gallery in London there are all kinds of activities during term-time and holidays. You might get the chance to dress up in the costumes of long ago, like these boys and girls.

Illustration from photographs supplied by the National Gallery.

These girls are working at the Worcester Royal Porcelain Company, making and painting some of the most delicate and beautiful china in the world. Visitors are welcome to look around the factory and also to see the Dyson Perrins Museum of Worcester Porcelain nearby. It's a fascinating day out, but please book in advance as a quarter of a million people visit there every year. The address is:- Dyson Perrins Museum, Severn Street, Worcester WR1 2NE.

Photographs by courtesy of the Worcester Royal Porcelain Company Ltd.

Meet Jonathon R. Lister Smith, a Master Farrier, who works full-time at the Museum of East Anglian Life at Stowmarket in Suffolk. You can see him at work and look at the interesting display of the farrier's craft through the ages. You can even have your horse shod, if you make an appointment!

Photograph by courtesy of the Museum of East Anglian Life, Stowmarket.

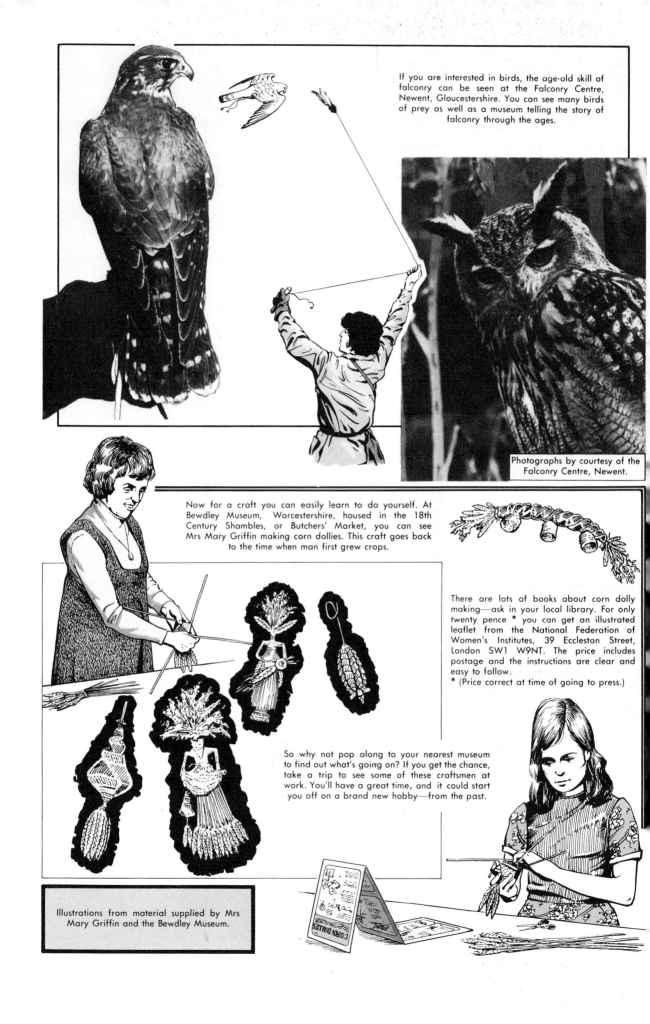

If you are interested in birds, the age-old skill of falconry can be seen at the Falconry Centre, Newent, Gloucestershire. You can see many birds of prey as well as a museum telling the story of falconry through the ages.

Photographs by courtesy of the Falconry Centre, Newent.

Now for a craft you can easily learn to do yourself. At Bewdley Museum, Worcestershire, housed in the 18th Century Shambles, or Butchers' Market, you can see Mrs Mary Griffin making corn dollies. This craft goes back to the time when man first grew crops.

There are lots of books about corn dolly making—ask in your local library. For only twenty pence * you can get an illustrated leaflet from the National Federation of Women's Institutes, 39 Eccleston Street, London SW1 W9NT. The price includes postage and the instructions are clear and easy to follow.
* (Price correct at time of going to press.)

So why not pop along to your nearest museum to find out what's going on? If you get the chance, take a trip to see some of these craftsmen at work. You'll have a great time, and it could start you off on a brand new hobby—from the past.

Illustrations from material supplied by Mrs Mary Griffin and the Bewdley Museum.

# The Summer Princess

CENTURIES ago, Bride, Princess of Summer, dressed the green glens of Scotland in flowers and sunlight.

One evening, as she passed the Well of Youth, she was stopped by an aged crone.

Bride, Princess of Summer, give me water, I beg of you.

Gladly, old mother.

Suddenly, a chill wind blew down the glen.

How strange. It has suddenly grown cold.

Give me the cup.

As she drank the magic water, the crone changed until Bride recognised her as Beira, the dreaded Queen of Winter, whose hammer had the power to destroy, and whose piercing, one-eyed glance turned all to ice. Wind and storm lived in her long black hair, and lightning grew from her fingers.

Beira, Queen of Winter!

Fool! Did you think to escape me for ever?

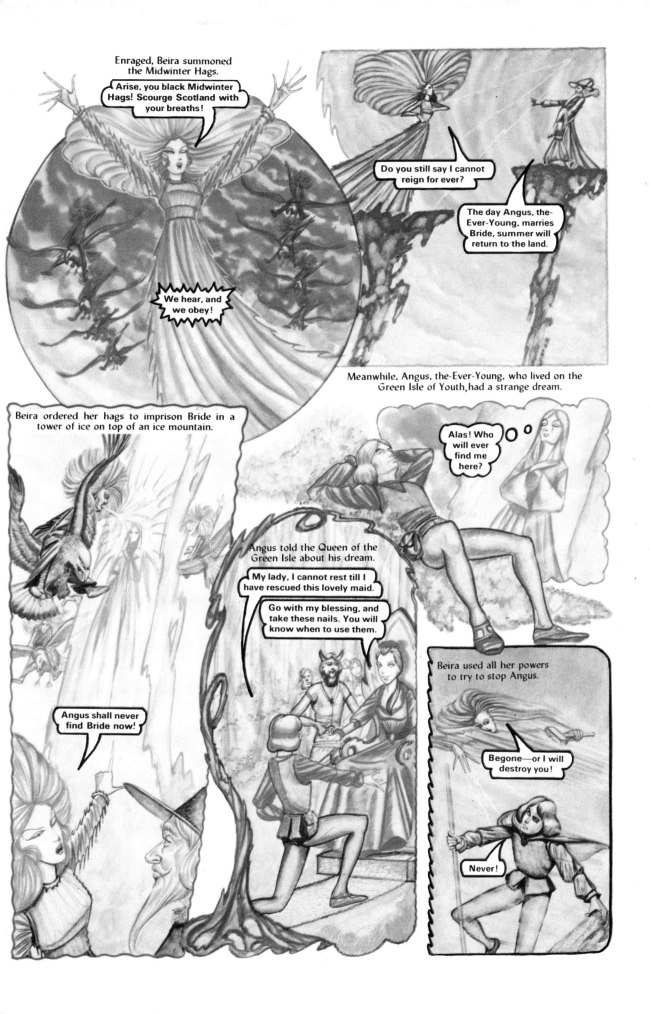

# YOUR LIFE IN YOUR HAND

Ever wondered what makes you tick? Look at your hands and you might be in for a surprise! Your left hand shows the qualities you were born with, your right hand shows what you have made of your life—and what's ahead!

## POINTED

Do you have pointed fingers? They are the mark of an artist; an inventor; someone bursting with ideas or with good intuition. An idealist, you have a vivid imagination and great psychic awareness. You love luxury, have great impulsiveness and a lively, charming personality.

## SQUARE

If you have squared-off fingertips, you are poised and methodical, with a love of justice and order. You have a strong sense of duty, and a lot of common-sense, but perhaps lack initiative. A very square middle finger shows intolerance.

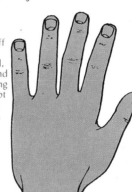

*Not every hand will be completely pointed, square, conical or spatulate—yours may have fingers of varying kinds, so you will have qualities from more than one category. For a detailed analysis, see the foot of the page.*

## CONICAL

Is your hand partly square, partly pointed? This shows equal amounts of reason and intuition. You are talented and understanding, and the first to admit a mistake. Friendly, you like peace and harmony, and enjoy comfort.

## SPATULATE

If you have spatulate-shaped fingers, with almost flat nail joints, you often act without thinking, only to regret it later. You are fond of the outdoors and travel, like active games and pastimes and want freedom above everything.

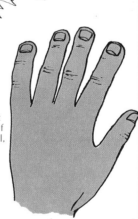

## FIRST FINGER

POINTED—Artistic.
CONICAL—Simplicity, fondness for reading.
SQUARE—Orderliness, love of regularity.
SPATULATE—You could be clairvoyant.
STRAIGHT, UPRIGHT—Independence.
SHORT—Ambitious.

## MIDDLE FINGER

POINTED—Intuition.
SQUARE—Self-discipline.
SPATULATE—A taste for study.
LONG—Pride.
SHORT—Thriftiness.

## RING FINGER

POINTED—Good fortune.
CONICAL—Business sense.
SQUARE—Love of riches.
SPATULATE—Love of dancing and the theatre.
SHORT—Indifference to fame.
LONG—Extravagant, loving fame and glamour.

## LITTLE FINGER

POINTED OR CONICAL—Eloquence, wisdom.
SQUARE OR SPATULATE—Physical skill.
SHORT—Quick to learn.
LONG—Thoughtful.

This hand diagram shows the meaning of each finger joint. The longer and thicker each part of your finger is, the more of its special quality you possess. For example, a long middle thumb joint means that you are a very logical person, a short middle thumb joint shows that you are not logical at all!

## VENUS

This mount, at the base of the thumb, is the largest on the hand. It shows love, vitality and pleasure, and, if this mount is plump and well-developed, you will enjoy life, finding much affection and many friends.

## JUPITER

Below the first finger, this mount, if well-developed, shows great ambition, rewarded by honour and happiness. Success is shown by straight upward lines, and lucky you if you find a star here—it's the sign of complete satisfaction in life.

## SATURN

Your destiny is shown by this mount, and if it is smooth and plain, you will have a quiet life. A triangle indicates that you are very interested in the occult. A well-developed mount shows that you tend to take life too seriously.

## SUN

This mount, below your ring finger, relates to artistic learnings, wealth and glory. A normal mount means that you have all these things in moderation. Cross lines could mean that a small obstacle lies in your path, and a triangle shows that you have artistic talent.

## MERCURY

Intelligence, business abilities, eloquence—all these are indicated on this mount. A triangle means that you may be successful in politics or diplomacy. Vertical lines mean that you have a leaning towards medicine—you could make an ideal nurse

## MOON

If this part of your hand is well-developed, you have a good imagination, and poetic tendencies. You dream a lot and may have premonitions. A romantic, you're altogether a mysterious personality.

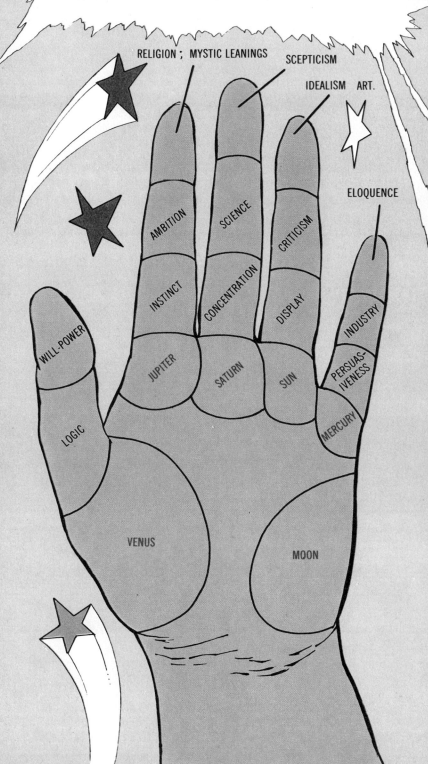

RELIGION ; MYSTIC LEANINGS
SCEPTICISM
IDEALISM ART.
ELOQUENCE
AMBITION
SCIENCE
CRITICISM
INSTINCT
CONCENTRATION
DISPLAY
INDUSTRY
WILL-POWER
JUPITER
SATURN
SUN
PERSUAS-IVENESS
LOGIC
MERCURY
VENUS
MOON

If you study them closely, the lines on your hand can reveal much about you. They show all that has happened to you during your life, and, if they are well-marked and strong, they can give an indication of your future. For instance, a strong Line of Head means that you have great willpower and courage, and will use your brain to its best advantage. Take a good look at your Line of Heart. It may fade in places and become stronger in others, foretelling the ups and downs of life, its joys and sorrows. An even line means an even life, with no great unhappiness. See if you can interpret the lines on your hand—what you learn may surprise you!

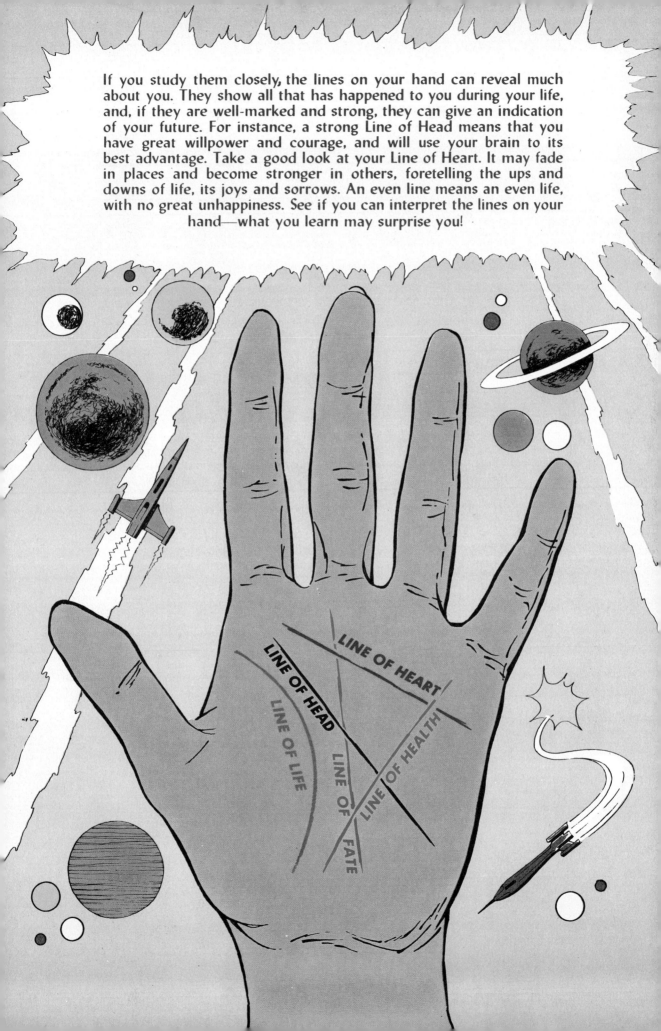

LINE OF HEART

LINE OF HEAD

LINE OF HEALTH

LINE OF LIFE

LINE OF FATE

# CAT OUT OF NOWHERE

I TURNED my head slowly, and looked at the row of birthday cards. Altogether there were six; five depicting cats, and one with 'Happy Birthday, 14-year-old' printed boldly in red. I picked up the nearest, a very large one.

It had a red background with a blue flower, and looking inquisitively out at me was a small tabby kitten. Like Tim.

Those words flitted through my mind and my eyes filled with tears. Tim had been my own kitten. I can still remember him lying in his little cat basket, too tired to play, or so I thought.

"We'll have to take him to the vet, dear," my mother said.

Which we did. And I can see, in my mind's eye, the vet looking at Tim. He stroked him, almost like a sign of farewell. Then he looked up at me.

"I think it's feline enteritis," he said slowly.

"Is there any chance of recovery?" Mum asked, stressing the last word.

The vet shook his head. The picture changed in my head, and I could see us leaving the surgery, me crying bitterly. I kept thinking of the way Tim's eyes, sea green and pathetic, stared at me as if to say, "Don't leave me. Don't go." As if he knew I was leaving him forever . . .

I blinked, and returned to the present. I didn't want birthday cards, not now—not ever. My Tim was gone. I stood the card I was holding on the shelf with its fellows. Then I looked at it in surprise.

The kitten on the card was moving!

"Impossible," I told myself, backing into a chair.

But the kitten leapt out of the card, down from the shelf and on to my lap. I stared at the little warm body that curled itself up on my lap.

"I'm going mad!" I gasped.

The tabby purred, its piercing eyes looking into mine. I stroked it, feeling the small bones beneath the soft fur. How long I sat there I don't know, but the next thing I knew, my mother was coming in through the door.

"I haven't been long, dear . . ." she began, then stopped, seeing the curled-up kitten nestled against my arm.

"Where . . . ?" she muttered.

I didn't know what to say. How could I tell her this kitten jumped out of a birthday card?

"It's . . . it's a stray, I think," I said lamely. "It miaowed at the back door."

Mum smiled. "I'm so glad," she said, "I thought you'd never . . ."

Then she hugged me, realising I'd got over Tim. I never did tell her about the birthday card. Who'd believe a story like that?

But I knew it was true, because that night I looked again at that card. The background was the same, the blue flowers still bloomed. But the little tabby kitten, the exact replica of the one I held in my arms, was gone . . .

I looked down at the kitten. Its fathomless eyes looked into mine. Then it tilted its head, looked at the empty birthday card, sighed and contentedly closed its eyes.

# BRIGHT IDEAS FOR A RAINY DAY

## Silver Bells

To make these little decorations, all you need are clean, dry egg-shells broken near the narrow end.

Trim the ragged edge with small scissors and make a small hole in the round end. Paint the shell inside and out and set aside to dry. When the paint is dry, put a little glue along the edge and dip the shell in glitter. Take a length of thread and knot the ends together. Pull the loop through a bead or sequin and knot the thread again 1.5—2 cms. from the bead or sequin. Pull the thread through the hole in the rounded end of the shell as far as the knot then make a knot on top of the shell and there you have a neat little bell ornament.

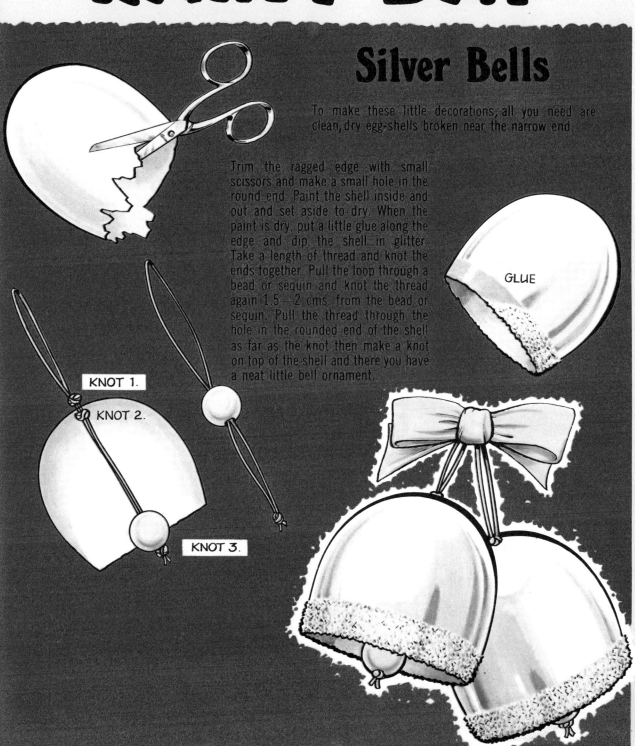

GLUE

KNOT 1.

KNOT 2.

KNOT 3.

# Patterned Eggs

ONION-SKIN DYE.
You need the dry, brown, outer skins of onions—enough to fill a large paper bag. Put the skins in an OLD pot and cover with water. Bring to the boil, then let them simmer for about an hour. (Get an adult to help you with this.) When the water is cool, strain it into a bowl, and throw away the skins. Put the dye back into the pot.

To make these pretty patterned eggs, first of all cut the legs of an old pair of tights into lengths a little longer than the eggs you are using. Lay little flowers or leaves on fresh white eggs then carefully put them in the stocking tube and tie both ends tightly. Put the eggs into the onion dye. Bring it to the boil and allow it to simmer for half an hour. When the eggs are cool enough to handle, remove the stockings and your eggs should be dyed leaving the pattern of the plant material either white or a pale colour.

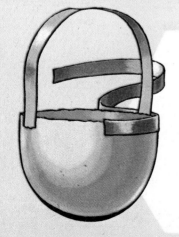

# Baskets

These little basket ornaments are made from half egg-shells using the rounded end only. Trim the ragged edge with scissors, then paint the shell inside and out and set aside to dry. Take a length of ribbon and glue the ends to the shell to form a handle. Take a second length of ribbon and glue it round the edge of the shell, and either tie it into a bow or glue a ready-made bow in place.

# Pear Pincushion

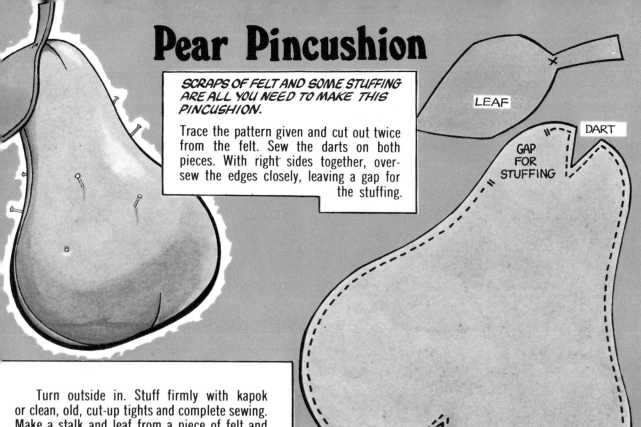

*SCRAPS OF FELT AND SOME STUFFING ARE ALL YOU NEED TO MAKE THIS PINCUSHION.*

Trace the pattern given and cut out twice from the felt. Sew the darts on both pieces. With right sides together, oversew the edges closely, leaving a gap for the stuffing.

LEAF

DART

GAP FOR STUFFING

DART

Turn outside in. Stuff firmly with kapok or clean, old, cut-up tights and complete sewing. Make a stalk and leaf from a piece of felt and stitch them to the top of the pear, ensuring that the leaf covers the stuffing hole stitching, and there's your pear pincushion ready for pins.

# Handy Bag

Take two pieces of the material with right sides together and, beginning 8 cms. from the top, sew round three sides, 1·5 cms. from the edge, stopping 8 cms. from the end and rounding the bottom corners.
Repeat with the two pieces of lining.
Trim the bottom corners of both bags and put one inside the other, wrong sides together.

You will need four pieces of material each 50 cms. by 36 cms. wide (or two pieces of material and two pieces of lining) and a pair of handles, which can be bought in any craft shop .

Having turned in 1·5 cms. on the 8 cms. left previously on the bags, sew the two bags together as shown. Put the top edges through the handles and turn under a small hem before hemming into place.

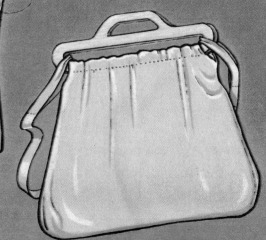

you have any long strips of material left, you can,
ou wish, make long handles to add to the bag.
can use the bag for carrying your swimming gear,
a knitting bag or just as a handy hold-all. Why not
ke a few and give them as presents?

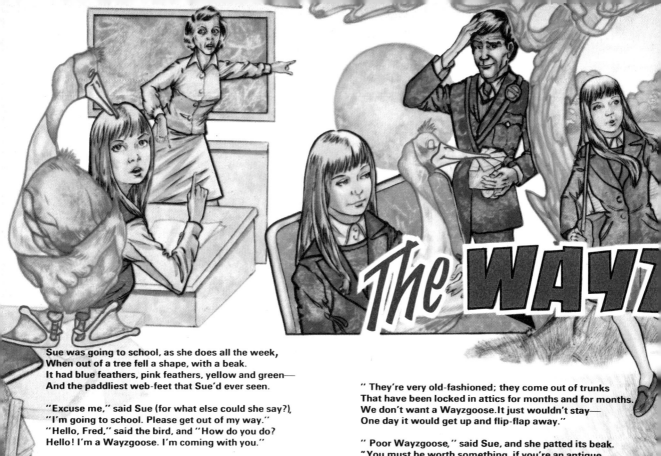

# The WAY[Z]

Sue was going to school, as she does all the week,
When out of a tree fell a shape, with a beak.
It had blue feathers, pink feathers, yellow and green—
And the paddliest web-feet that Sue'd ever seen.

"Excuse me," said Sue (for what else could she say?),
"I'm going to school. Please get out of my way."
"Hello, Fred," said the bird, and "How do you do?
Hello! I'm a Wayzgoose. I'm coming with you."

"What's that?" cried the teacher. "Who brought that big bird?"
Sue stood by her desk. She said not a word.
But the Wayzgoose, behind her, tapped on her head.
"I came here with Fred. And I'm staying," he said.

"My name is not Fred," said Sue, "and what's more—
The Wayzgoose, it followed me here. It's a bore."
The teacher said: "Really? In that case, it's clear,
You must go to the zoo; it will follow you there."

So Sue and the Wayzgoose squeezed onto a bus;
She bought seven tickets to save any fuss.
"Excuse me, Zookeeper," Sue said with some pride,
"I've come with a Wayzgoose. It's waiting outside."

"It keeps calling me Fred. But my name is Sue."
"Ah, yes," said the Zookeeper, "I thought that you knew.
A Wayzgoose is muddled, deep down in its head.
I had one that called my great-grandmother Fred."

"They're very old-fashioned; they come out of trunks
That have been locked in attics for months and for months.
We don't want a Wayzgoose. It just wouldn't stay—
One day it would get up and flip-flap away."

"Poor Wayzgoose," said Sue, and she patted its beak.
"You must be worth something, if you're an antique.
We'll go to the junk-shop and see if they can
Find you a home with a rich, kindly man."

"Ah, yes," said the junk-shop man, jingling his money.
"I'll buy him. How much? It's really quite funny.
We wanted a stuffed Wayzgoose to stand by the gate.
This one will do nicely. We'll get him in shape."

"But this one's not stuffed! He's alive and he's well!"
Cried Sue, with some heat. "And if you think I'd sell
My Wayzgoose for stuffing—I'll kick up a row!
No! You leave that Wayzgoose the way he is now!"

So Sue and the Wayzgoose walked back to the town.
They went to the pet-shop to see Mrs Brown.
"No! No!" cried she, climbing up onto a shelf.
"A Wayzgoose? No, thanks! You can keep it yourself!"

# GOOSE

"The last one I had let out all the rabbits,
And painted a tortoise. It had such strange habits.
Look after it well, it's a very fine goose—
Although I admit that it isn't much use."

"Oh, Wayzgoose," said Sue, " I wish you could see
Just what a nuisance you're being to me.
You're really quite nice, but what can I do?
I think the police ought to know about you."

"A Wayzgoose?" the policeman said. " They're very rare.
They grow on baked-bean trees, and are seldom seen here."
"He's tame," said Sue, hopefully. " And friendly, too.
Put him in a cell and he'll be friends with you."

"Oh, no," said the policeman. " That cannot be done.
He isn't a robber. He's not on the run.
Just being around's not a crime, as you know.
I think you must keep him till he wants to go."

And so, Sue took the Wayzgoose home. 'Twas happy as could be.
It asked to have its toenails cut, and ate a cake for tea.
Sue's mother didn't like it. " Oh, really, Sue, " she said.
" Why is it here? Why won't it go? Why does it call me Fred?"

She telephoned the Council, and asked for Pest Control,
" We've got a pest , a Wayzgoose. Much worse than a mole.
Please come at once and bring a net. It may need many men
To catch this most peculiar bird and put it in a pen!"

" A Wayzgoose?" said the Council man, "You'll have to tell us more.
Its name, its size, its weight, and where it lived before."
" It's big and broad," said Mother. " Its eyes are rather sweet.
It's sitting on my knitting and it's got size seven feet."

" I fear we cannot help you," said the Council man with glee.
" Our Wayzgoose trapper disappeared in nineteen-forty- three.
A Wayzgoose always knows just where a Wayzgoose wants to stay.
Keep your Wayzgoose warm. He will drive the moths away."

And so the Wayzgoose stayed with Sue until the end of March.
It learnt to cook, it wrote a book, and even cleaned the bath.
And just when Sue was thinking that she'd found a lifelong friend,
What had to happen happened—as it had to in the end.

" I'm sorry, Fred," the Wayzgoose said, shuffling its feet.
" My time is up. I have to leave, on Wednesday next week.
I have to fly to Egypt (his wing brushed away a tear),
The Wayzgoose Annual Meeting's at the Pyramids this year."

On Wednesday all Sue's family came out to say goodbye.
They shook the Wayzgoose by the foot , it leapt into the sky.
And then the Wayzgoose dipped its wings, flew on and on and on—
And the thing about a Wayzgoose is—you miss it when it's gone.

# HORSE POWER through the Ages

Part 2

Everyone knows what this cart or wagon is. It's the pioneer wagon that carried settlers across the Prairies of America. It was a roughly-made cart but it stood up to the job it had to do.

In America in 1880, horses were used to pull fire engines. This illustration shows one such powerful team in action.

Although nowadays cars and buses are used in most countries, some remote countries such as in the Himalayas, still use a horse litter as transport.

In some areas of China these picturesque carts were used as taxis. Although the local horses could withstand frost, they were affected by heat and rain, therefore the shelter was rigged up.

Although most heavy transport these days is done by lorries, many firms still have some of the old-fashioned carts in use especially for publicity stunts and advertising.